FAIRFIELD PORTER
A Catalogue Raisonné of His Prints

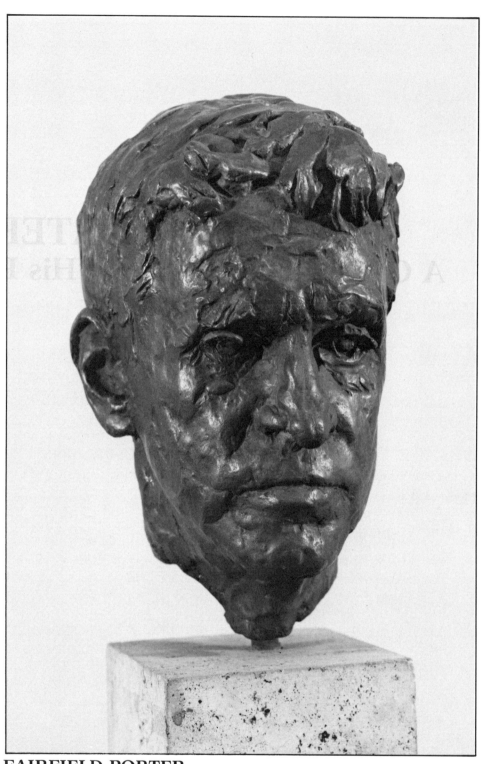

FAIRFIELD PORTER

Cast bronze by Robert Winthrop White 1970. Collection of the
Heckscher Museum,
Huntington, New York.

FAIRFIELD PORTER
A Catalogue Raisonné of His Prints
including illustrations, bookjackets and exhibition posters

by
JOAN LUDMAN

*with appreciations by David Shapiro and Brooke Alexander and
an interview with Jane Freilicher by Fred Deitzel*

Highland House Publishing, Inc. — Westbury, N.Y.

First Printing

Printed in the United States of America

Library of Congress Cataloging in Publication Data

Ludman, Joan.
    Fairfield Porter, a catalogue raisonne of his prints,
including illustrations, bookjackets, and exhibition
posters.

    Bibliography: p.
    Includes indexes.
    1. Porter, Fairfield—Catalogs.   I. Title
NE539.P57A4   1981   769.92′4   81-4150
ISBN 0-938988-00-X   AACR2

ISBN 0-938988-00-X

4

DEDICATION

For Harold, Evette and Neil, Wendy and Mark
my beloved family
to whom I present this book
on a beloved subject.

CONTENTS

Color plates follow page 32

Other works by Joan Ludman

Print Reference Sources: A Selected Bibliography, 18th-20th Centuries. Compiled by Lauris Mason and Joan Ludman. Kraus-Thomson Organization, Limited, Millwood, New York 1975. Revised and Enlarged edition, 1979.

Print Collector's Quarterly: An Anthology of Essays on Eminent Printmakers of the World. Edited by Lauris Mason and Joan Ludman. KTO Press, Millwood, New York, 1977.

The Lithographs of George Bellows: A Catalogue Raisonné. By Lauris Mason. Assisted by Joan Ludman. KTO Press, Millwood, New York, 1977.

Fine Prints: Collecting, Buying and Selling. Cecile Shapiro and Lauris Mason. With foreign language glossary by Joan Ludman. Harper and Row, New York, 1976. Paperbound edition: Cornerstone Press, New York, 1978.

ACKNOWLEDGMENTS

My interest in and admiration for the work of Fairfield Porter is deep and of long standing. My acquaintance with him, though all too brief, was greatly inspiring. The making of this book has been a joyous task. My ever-widening contacts with so many who knew, worked with and loved Porter have rewarded me with a more revealing look and warm understanding of the man, his life, and his work.

I am deeply grateful to:

Mrs. Fairfield Porter, Anne, a great lady, a dear and gentle woman, who has always been generously supportive. She made available to me the archival collection of Fairfield Porter Papers. She has given of her time, her knowledge, her reminiscences, her caring, and her sincere encouragement.

Lauris Mason, my friend and editor, who urged me to embark upon this project; and whose wise counsel, unfailing assurances, and confidence in my knowledge and capabilities accompanied me all along the way.

Philip Ferrato, without whose constant aid and advice, cooperation and sharing of materials, this book could not have come into being.

Benedict Leerburger, editor-in-chief, whose skillfull guidance and diligence saw this project through to its completion.

Carolyn and Brooke Alexander, and Michael Heming, veritable repositories of information, readily imparting facts and figures and myriad essential details in documentation of the lithographic *oeuvre.*

Paul Cummings, whose *Oral History* interview with Fairfield Porter, conducted in June, 1968 for the Archives of American Art, Smithsonian Institution, will always serve as the basis for all scholarly investigation into Porter's life and work.

Kenneth Wiggins Porter, Professor of History, Emeritus, University of Oregon, for a most enlightening and delightful correspondence concerning the era of the *Vanguard Verse* publications.

Professor Alan Wald, Department of English Language and Literature, University of Michigan, for his erudite writings on the poet John Wheelwright.

Clifton Jones, curator of manuscripts, The John Hay Library of Brown University; Rosemary Cullen of the Library, and Neil Ludman, for their help and patience in researching the Wheelwright papers.

Jennifer Melby, who almost from the very beginning patiently helped in all the "detective work" I asked of her, and supplied vitally important information about the ateliers and workshops.

Chip Elwell, who graciously lent his expertise in the technological aspects of lithography.

Dianne Ludman, my "Chicago connection," for utilizing her expert research abilities on behalf of this project.

Louise Dunn Yochim, of the Chicago Society of Artists, for providing information about that august organization.

Jules Sherman and Reginald Pollack, who gave generously of their time and extensive knowledge in the course of interviews and correspondence regarding the paper-offset lithographs.

Rackstraw Downes, artist and writer, and the many others who so kindly lent the Porter letters in their possession.

Laurence Korwin, Special Projects Group, Chicago, for making available to me the Bicentennial Poster and information pertaining to it.

Elizabeth E. Roth, Keeper of Prints, and Robert Rainwater, New York Public Library, and William McNaught, Archives of American Art, New York, for aiding my research in their respective institutions.

David Shapiro, Brooke Alexander, Jane Freilicher and Fred Deitzel, for contributing their exceptional, perceptive essays to this volume.

All those who extended to me the courtesy of granting interviews, or who sent letters, or who helped in innumerable ways: Frances Badger, Ted Berrigan, Jane Freilicher, George Goodstadt, Robert Keene, Dr. Daniel Mason, Paul Narkiewicz, Ron Padgett, Jean-Pierre Rémond, Prescott Schutz, Peter Tatistcheff.

Ruth Janssen, dear friend, for the many hours spent putting the manuscript together, for endless typing, for always being ready to lend a hand, an ear, or a shoulder.

My family, who sincerely shared in my enthusiasm for my subject and my work, and who pretended not to mind the many, many months that my attentions were diverted from them.

Joan Ludman

Fairfield Porter as Printmaker

About Tolstoy's remark ["a good work of art can in its entirety be represented only by itself"] and its implications for translation: it does not mean that one work of art cannot have a family resemblance to another. The content of art is an aspect of vitality; the translation has to have its independent vitality. Making lithographs means translation from a painting or preparatory sketches which themselves (one hopes) are art. But it is good insofar as it has this independent life.[1]

Over the course of his lifetime, Fairfield Porter produced thirty-one prints, some with additional states, all in varying edition sizes, bringing the totality of his output to approximately 2200 extant impressions, in addition to 4000 impressions of the large edition calendar prints. The graphic *oeuvre* includes early linoleum block prints, paper-offset lithographs and a single silkscreen, as well as the fourteen color lithographs executed in the last six years of his life, at the height of his artistic powers.

Fairfield Porter was born in 1907 in Winnetka, Illinois, a privileged suburb of Chicago. He grew up in a comfortable, warm family environment with his parents, three brothers, and a sister. His father's interest in art and architecture and his mother's interest in language and writing were major influences upon him as a child. When very young, he enjoyed looking at paintings at the Art Institute of Chicago, and at the age of twelve or thirteen he was already an admirer of Rockwell Kent and Pablo Picasso.

Porter's architect father, a prominent designer of Greek Revival houses, bought Great Spruce Head Island in 1912. Beginning in the summer of his sixth year, Fairfield Porter spent most of the summers of his life on this much beloved island off the Maine coast. Images of the island, its structures and surrounding meadows and waters, would be a major source for his drawings and paintings.

A trip to Europe with his family when he was fourteen introduced him to Leonardo and Titian, Veronese and Turner. From 1924 to 1928, Porter was a student at Harvard University, where he studied with Arthur Pope and Arthur Kingsley Porter in the arts, and with Alfred North Whitehead in philosophy. In his junior year he contributed an illustration to the *Harvard Lampoon*. (See Fig. I). Since it is signed with the initials "R.F." as well as "F.P.," it is likely that a fellow student collaborated in the conception of the cartoon

After his junior year at Harvard, Porter spent the summer of 1927 travelling through France and Germany and then spent five weeks in the Soviet Union. He accompanied a neighbor from Winnetka who was travelling with a group of American journalists, economists, and labor leaders. In Moscow he saw the famed and memorable Shchukin collection of modern art. The trip to Russia had a significant influence upon his early political thinking. He admired the ideal of the non-exploitation of men by other men, and he developed a lifelong antipathy towards totalitarianism in all its forms.

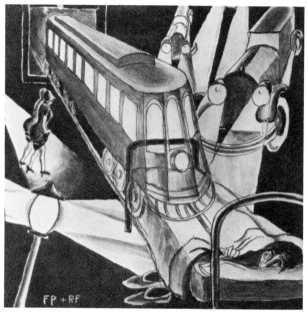

Fig. 1
That first night in Mowrer Hall, or
that Massachusetts Avenue bedroom.
Illustration for *Harvard Lampoon,* November 3rd, 1927.
Volume 94, number 3, page 96.

Fig. II
Three Arrows

After his graduation from Harvard, friends in New York induced Porter to attend the Art Students League, where he remained for two years, studying with Boardman Robinson and Thomas Hart Benton. He respected the individualized teaching methods of the former far more than Benton's inflexible system. While living in New York, Porter made the acquaintance of the painter John Marin, who remained an artist he deeply admired for his originality of vision and his characteristic unprecedented style of syncopation, "angular askewness," and fragmentation.

Upon leaving the League, Porter made an extended trip through Italy in 1931. While there, he met Bernard Berenson, for whose writing and thinking in art and aesthetics he developed a lifelong respect. In Rome, Porter created his first lithograph, an illustration for Fyodor Dostoyevsky's *The Possessed* (See L.1). Among the Fair-

field Porter Papers there still exists a lengthy, painstakingly hand-
written and detailed summary of this novel, done in preparation for
his eventually abandoned attempt to illustrate the entire narrative.
The Russian novel had always been preeminent in his literary tastes.

In 1932, upon his return from Italy, the poet Anne Channing and
Fairfield Porter were married. He settled in New York, and studied
anatomy at the School of Medicine of Cornell University when New
York was in the depths of the Depression. Through a friend from Art
Students League days, he became involved in radical politics and the
Socialist Party, though he never became a member. His first teaching
experience was gained at drawing classes at the Rebel Arts Center,
an organization of "artists in all fields affiliated with or sympathetic
to the socialist and bona fide labor movement." At an editorial meet-
ing of its short-lived periodical *Arise,* a socialist imitation of *The New
Masses,* Porter met the outstanding rebel poet John Brooks Wheelwright, a Boston Brahmin turned revolutionary. " . . . I was always
interested in poets. . . . and Wheelwright's poetry I had read and admired before I met him. And I think it's because I am somewhat in
awe of any writer of poetry."[2] (Henry Wadsworth Longfellow was a
distant relative of Porter's and T.S. Eliot a second cousin.)

In 1934, Wheelwright initiated the publication of a series of
pamphlets called *Poems for a Dime* and *Poems for 2 Bits.* He wrote to
Porter " . . . I am sure that some illustrations by you would help the
sale of the magazine . . . I can pay you only in complimentary
copies, but I can pay you for the materials if you want me to . . ."[3]
Porter answered, "I can do linoleum cuts (once long ago I made
one). Don't send me proofs of Whelan or the next number. I would
rather first look at already published poems for ideas. Then I will
know better what I can or can not do; for instance, I mightn't
understand the poems."[4]

Among Porter's first contributions to Wheelwright's *Vanguard
Verse* publications was *Three Arrows,* a stylized decoration for the
cover and title page of *Poems for a Dime,* January 8, 1936 issue (See
Fig. II). The three arrows were originally the symbol of the Social
Democratic Party of Austria. The Socialist Party in the United States
adopted their symbol as a tribute to their socialist militia, which, in
1934, was the first in Europe to resist the establishment of an
authoritarian state. Porter, however, expressed reservations about
the subject matter in a letter to Wheelwright: "I don't think arrows
are a good enough symbol because I doubt that they have enough
emotional adhesions for enough people."[5] He expanded on the
theme of the "three arrows" in the linoleum cut, *Three Archers* (See
L. 3), which was in the same issue. In another letter to Wheelwright, he wrote:

I am sending off two linoleum cuts, which will show

you what I can do . . . If the two proofs are dry I will enclose them in this letter. I learned to make proofs in 5th or 6th grade Grammar School. The printing course they gave made school resemble Soviet education, but since then the Winnetka schools have gone progressive, and in ·many respects are better, I guess; but instead of teaching printing they teach the kids to make their own toy boats, French, astronomy, and Football. . . . Now I can be more definite about illustrations. It takes me about a week to design and execute illustrations, so if you can send proofs to me not less than a week before your deadline I can send you cuts in time. Of course, I need to keep the page proofs long enough to read them only.

Let me know what you think of the cuts as illustrations and anything I should know about cutting lines deeper or shallower, and so on. . . .[6]

Porter continued to contribute his expressionistic linoleum cuts to these *Vanguard Verse* pamphlets sponsored by Wheelwright, until the last issue, *Poems for a Dime* of November 7, 1937.

Returning to Winnetka upon his grandmother's death in 1936, Porter and his family remained there, near his parents, for the next three years. At the Art Institute of Chicago in 1938, he saw an important exhibition of Vuillard and Bonnard. Vuillard especially earned Porter's abiding admiration throughout his life and deeply influenced his work. Many years later he remarked, "What I like in Vuillard is that it seems to be ordinary, what he's doing, but the extraordinary is everywhere."[7]

Living again in the Chicago area, Porter became a member of the Chicago Society of Artists, the oldest continuously active art organization in the United States. In a recent (1977) exhibition brochure, the Society is described:

Through the years the Chicago Society of Artists has nurtured its vitality, and by means of a careful jury system, resolutely maintained a consistency in the selection of its members, based only upon highly accepted professional standards. In this process, also, the group has aligned itself with progressive art movements in the nation. . . . The Society's role in generating and advancing the aesthetic goals of Chicago and the nation is correlative to the history of art in the United States since 1888. . . ."[8]

In addition to periodic group exhibitions, the Chicago Society publishes annually, since 1937, an original block-print calendar. Fairfield Porter contributed three linoleum block prints to this *Artists'*

Calendar, for the years 1939 and 1940 (See L. 8-10). The calendars were printed directly from the artists' original wood or linoleum blocks, in large limited editions of one thousand or two thousand impressions.

In 1939, Porter's first one-man show was arranged at the Winnetka Community House. His work was getting some exposure, though he was not yet well known. Porter's father died in 1939, and Fairfield and his family moved to Peekskill, New York. In the ensuing months, he met Willem de Kooning and Clement Greenberg, who were to play crucial parts in the development of his art. Porter claimed that he always remained a figurative painter simply *because* of critic Greenberg's authoritarian championing of abstraction over figurative painting. And "from de Kooning, Porter absorbed the elements that mark him as an artist much of the time: gesture, and the physical importance and integrity of the paint."[9]

During the war years, Porter lived and worked in New York City. Having studied mechanical drawing before and during World War II, he was employed by an industrial design firm which was working for the United States Navy. When the war was over, he studied for a time at the Parsons School of Design with a former Louvre art restorer, Jacques Maroger, who introduced him to his Maroger medium. Porter used this gel medium in his painting from that time on. He also worked with the Dutch painter Van Hooten, who praised the "light" in his paintings and encouraged spontaneity in Porter's work.

In 1949, Porter and his family moved to a comfortable, rambling old house near the ocean in Southampton, Long Island, New York, where he lived for the rest of his life. He began to exhibit at the Tibor de Nagy Gallery in New York City. At almost the same time, he became an editorial associate for *Art News*, remaining in that position until 1958. He continued to contribute articles until 1967. Porter told Paul Cummings in an interview in 1968: "I think I learned most as a painter from painters . . . from de Kooning and Van Hooten and Maroger and my own contemporaries now, Larry Rivers, Jane Freilicher, Alex Katz, John Button. I've learned a lot from all of those . . ."[10] His close friendships, developed during the 'fifties, grew to include the poets Frank O'Hara, Kenneth Koch, James Schuyler and John Ashbery. Porter told Cummings: "I once wrote poetry for a while. I started to do that because I met all those poets who were published by the Tibor de Nagy Gallery and they used to meet at the Cedar Bar and pull something out of their coat pockets and show them to each other. And I envied that very much. I thought I'd like to do that too. So I tried to see if I could and for a little while I could . . . it didn't sustain itself."[11] Toward the end of 1970, it occurred to the poet Ted Berrigan that he and Fairfield Porter could "make something together, since we were both there, that would be 'of' that particular time," in the tradition of Apollinaire, Reverdy, Juan Gris, and later Frank O'Hara and his group of poets and painters.[12] The first phrases of Berrigan's poem *Scorpion, Eagle and Dove* were composed as he approached a corner of Main Street in Southampton, the corner which Porter subsequently used as the site for his illustration. He made three versions of the drawing; the last was plate size, and was printed on a platen press owned by Robert Keene in Southampton (See Appendix II). In the 'seventies, Porter designed bookjackets for some of his poet friends (See Appendix I).

Porter became art critic for *The Nation* in 1959, and it was for an article on de Kooning in this periodical that he won the Longview Foundation Award in art criticism. Porter was consistently aware of the artistic issues of the time; he understood, respected and admired the Abstract Expressionists, though he himself continued to work in the figurative tradition. He told John Bernard Myers, "The important thing for critics to remember is the 'subject matter' in abstract painting and the 'abstraction' in representational work."[13]

Beginning in 1959, and through 1968, Porter consistently showed his work in the Whitney Museum Annuals in New York.

The late 'fifties and early 'sixties saw a tremendous proliferation of printmaking activity throughout the country. June Wayne's Tamarind Lithography Workshop in Los Angeles was established, as was Tatyana Grossman's Universal Limited Art Editions in West Islip, New York. These establishments and many others gave new life to and restored the prestige of art lithography in the United States. They encouraged artists and printers to master the medium, to experiment with it, and to cooperate with each other in order to expand the vast potential of the lithographic process. An appreciation was developed for the qualities, characteristics and possibilities of their material—the stone, the plate and the paper.

Contemporaneously with these developments, Porter embarked upon an innovative lithographic experiment. The artist Reginald Pollack was seeking a less costly method by which a larger body of work could be created in a shorter amount of time, without getting caught in the then current "quagmire of lithographic technology." He felt that it was the *technology* that was becoming of interest, rather than the work of art itself, and that under these conditions, the art lost its spontaneity.[14] He was convinced that fine original lithographs could be made more readily available to the public at comparatively little cost, if a technique were to be developed for producing them on high speed offset presses. Jules Sherman, who owned several large presses, was involved in a similar quest; he volunteered his presses and his expertise and joined Pollack in researching and developing this concept. Their efforts resulted in a process using the huge, three-roller offset presses, with the matrix a plate of plastic-impregnated paper sensitive to oil crayon. The artist worked directly upon these paper-offset plates that were of a composition which made it possible to wrap them around the cylinder of the press. There were no intervening photomechanical procedures. The three-roller process caused the final printed image to appear the same as the drawing on the original matrix, a feature which made this method attractive to novice printmakers.

Sherman and Pollack organized the experimental program, and taught this innovative technique to the artists, most of whom were new to printmaking. Highly personalized prints resulted. Fairfield Porter enjoyed the entire concept, an approach that allowed maximum spontaneity and a freedom comparable to drawing in his own sketchbooks. He liked the loose, fingerprinted, almost haphazard look of the finished lithograph. The direct quality of the medium, the paper plates, made it possible for him to select the best drawings. If the proofs were not satisfactory, they were torn up. Porter eventually produced six of these black and white offset lithographs (See L. 11-16). Speaking of them seven years later to Paul Cummings, he said, they:

> . . . were quite nice . . . they looked very good in a group show of prints. They stand out. . . . Reginald Pollack asked some people to do these things. They were put out in an edition. And I made some. Other people made some. That was one of the few times that I worked in a way that I don't usually do, which was—I got a system. You had to do these things on this sensitized paper and you mustn't get your fingerprints on it. The first ones did have fingerprints on them but they looked alright, you know, printed. And they wanted them to look spontaneous. They didn't want something that you figured out when you did it. So it was a spontaneous sketch. And I developed a system of drawing for this, and the system was roughly: . . . a line that I drew showed a change of color. That was its meaning. Not a change of form. I drew around the different colors. So it has roughly the look of a numbers painting, only it's better . . .[15]

Approximately forty artists were involved in the endeavor, eventually creating about 140 prints. Pollack recalls that they could "create in a day what Toulouse-Lautrec's printer took six months to do! At the end of a day, there was a small mountain of production."[16] Among the other artists who took part in this innovative program were Philip Pearlstein, Paul Resika, Harvey Dinnerstein and Jane Wilson (See also page 69). A large number of these works were subsequently acquired by Collectors Graphics and shown at the Peridot Gallery in New York, where they received critical plaudits.

In succeeding years, Porter's painting gained a great measure of recognition. In 1966, Hilton Kramer wrote:

> The pictures in Mr. Porter's latest exhibition, which opened this week at the Tibor de Nagy Gallery, include some of the best work the artist has ever produced. They are pictures that could only have been painted by an artist who had remained especially alert to the central artistic issues of his time, yet the pictures themselves exist at a considerable distance from those issues. Inevitably, then, our response to Mr. Porter's work will have much to do with our feelings about that distance.
>
> For here is an artist with an abiding loyalty to certain figures out of the painting of the last century and the early decades of this century, an artist in whose consciousness the felicitous precedents of Manet and Vuillard, of Monet and Sargent and Hopper, still act as a spur and a guide. Mr. Porter is an artist unembarrassed by good painterly manners; yet he is very far from being merely genteel . . . underlying the correctness of Mr. Porter's style, with its well-bred synthesis of French elegance and American dryness, one discerns a pictorial mind of unusual intelligence. This quality of intelligence is abetted by a fine sensitivity to the nuances of direct observation and both the intelligence and the sensitivity act as a brake against the painter's extraordinary facility.[17]

Porter was in demand during these years as a guest lecturer and visiting artist at many schools and universities throughout the country, including Southampton College of Long Island University, Queens College, Amherst College, Yale University, and the Skowhegan School of Painting and Sculpture. The Cleveland Museum of Fine Arts organized the first retrospective of his work in 1966.

In that year, Porter made the only silkscreen of his career (L. 17). Bright, flat-planed colors in an intimate setting distinguish this work and the stencil collage made in preparation for it. Though he never returned to this medium, and considered this single effort an experiment, the print is highly successful.

In 1968, Porter was one of ten artists whose work was selected to represent the United States at the 34th Venice Biennale. The others were Leonard Baskin, Byron Burford, Robert Cremean, Edwin Dickinson, Richard Diebenkorn, Frank Gallo, Red Grooms, James McGarrell and Reuben Nakian. During the same year, in the course of an interview with Paul Cummings, Porter expressed an interest in doing graphics again. In 1969, he began his tentative work in color lithography.

Toward the end of 1967, Jacques Mourlot, the son of the director of the Paris atelier Fernand Mourlot, established a lithographic workshop in New York in partnership with American interests. Shortly, however, the partnership was dissolved and Mourlot Graphics, Ltd. remained, as in France, a family enterprise. Among the artists who worked at the Mourlot shop in New York were Adolph Gottlieb, Roy Lichtenstein, Larry Rivers, Ben Shahn, and Jack Youngerman.

It was at Mourlot, in 1969, that Porter initiated his first venture into color lithography. He completed—but not entirely to his satisfaction—the lithograph *Street Scene* (L. 18), and requested of his publisher, Brooke Alexander, that it not be released. (He later pulled two or three proofs of a print, tentatively titled *Lizzie Drawing*, which once again he found unsatisfactory, and he never completed it.) In the trial proofs pulled prior to the printing of *Street Scene* (Figs. VII-X) we see Porter trying to abandon line in his effort to use *color* rather than drawing to control form. This he achieved in his next print.

Porter found conditions difficult at Mourlot Graphics. A certain tension existed in the workshop. When he was invited in June, 1970 by John Eastman, of the Skowhegan School of Painting and Sculpture, to contribute a print to a portfolio being published for the benefit of the school, he transferred his lithographic endeavors to the Bank Street Atelier, Ltd. (See L. 19). The Atelier, founded in February 1969, occupied handsome, spacious quarters in a building which had previously been a U.S. Naval Hospital. Porter found the beautiful physical plant, its large windows and light, its space, and its friendly atmosphere conducive to his printmaking activities. It had three floors which housed offices, individual cubicles for artists to work in (Porter had his own cubicle), and large quarters for the flat-bed machines and proofing presses.

Porter was an enthusiastic printmaker; he enjoyed the technicians and made the effort to speak with the French technicians in their own language. He took pleasure in the camaraderie of working along with other people—the printers, the pressmen, the *chromiste*—which the process of printmaking necessitates, in contrast to the solitude of painting. Jennifer Melby, the production assistant at the Bank Street Atelier, recalls that whereas some printmakers liked to have certain preliminary processes already accomplished by the time they arrived to work on their lithographs, Porter liked to have a hand in every step of the way and liked learning each aspect of producing the print. During the proofing, he worked very closely with the printer assigned to him. The workmen waited for him to arrive in the morning before beginning the most preliminary of procedures. He hovered around the press, joining and becoming part of the crew (See Fig. III). In turn, the technicians held Porter in high regard as a person and as an artist. They felt he had a real grasp for the medium, and that technically he continued to improve. Porter wrote "The technicians at Bank Street helped me, I learned a lot, and I am very pleased with the results. One of the French technicians there had worked with Vuillard. He must have been only a boy, because he looks about 45 now. I asked him, 'Vous avez connu Vuillard?' 'Non, je ne l'ai pas connu,' and then as an after thought, realizing the difference between American and French manners, 'J'ai parlé avec lui.' "[18]

Fig. III
At the Bank Street Atelier

Porter is comparing a proof with a watercolor study. Jean-Pierre Rémond, *chromiste*, is holding a color sample next to the watercolor for Porter's approval. Mauro Guiffreda is on the left, mixing the colors.

Before starting work on each lithograph, Porter painted a watercolor of the planned image. Chip Elwell, curator at Bank Street at the time Porter was working there, writes:

> The technical means Porter chose to finesse fresh, clear prints was the careful application and control of tusche, a greasy solution of water and black pigment. The prints relate strongly to his water colors in their technical approach, but differ importantly in that they depend heavily on overprinting, involve a basically subtractive approach, and work within strict palette choices.
> Porter painted his stones and plates with tusche, using

stronger or weaker solutions to give varying amounts of his final choice of color for each individual plate. Once drawn, the plates are fresh looking and the possibilities for changing the color to be printed are still open, but possibilities for changing the image are narrow if the freshness is to be maintained. In direct contrast to water color they are all subtractive. Local areas of any color might still be restrained or removed altogether with acid, but precise color choices are limited to the number of plates printed. The subtlety, richness, and deceptive simplicity that Porter maintained were the results of carefully engineering the available combinations that overprinting afford. In the area above the table surface in *The Table*, for instance, Porter

Fig. IV
At the Bank Street Atelier

Porter is studying a proof pulled from the stone. Behind him, on the wall, is the original watercolor study and another proof.

dumped everything available and then carefully removed to approach the value of temperature he wanted.[19]

The portfolio "Ten Lithographs by Ten Artists," which included Porter's *The Dog at the Door* (Fig. IV and L. 19), was published in 1971 shortly after the Bank Street Atelier had become the Shorewood Atelier, Inc. in August of that year. Published for the benefit of the Skowhegan School in Maine, other contributors included Jack Beal, James Brooks, Red Grooms, Chaim Gross, Philip Guston, Alex Katz, Richard Lindner, Robert Andrew Parker and Philip Pearlstein. With Porter's *Dog at the Door* we see the emergence of his style—the abandonment of line drawing and the use of color to control form.

At Bank Street in January, 1971, Porter began work on *The Table* (L. 20), *The Christmas Tree* (L. 21), and *Girl in the Woods* (L. 22). In April, he started work on *Sixth Avenue*, first and second states (L. 23). By May, he had completed the entire group of five lithographs. *South Meadow* (L. 24) and *Broadway* (L.25), completed in 1972, were the last prints Porter produced at the Bank Street Atelier.

Jean-Pierre Rémond, who had been technical director and chromiste at Bank Street, and Yann Samson also from Bank Street, subsequently set up their own workshop, Resam Press, on 11th Street in New York. Porter, who had worked particularly closely with Rémond, produced his next three lithographs at Resam. *Ocean* (first and second states, L. 26) was the sole lithograph done in 1973. The entire edition of 85 impressions was donated by Porter for the benefit of the Skowhegan Scholarship Fund. Both states of *Ocean, Ocean II* (L. 27) done in 1974 and the three states of *Apple Blossoms* (L. 28) 1974 were printed at Resam Press. In addition to *Ocean II* and *Apple Blossoms, Sunrise* (L. 29) was also done in 1974. However, it was printed by Yann Samson who had by now established his own press in New York.

In 1974-75 a retrospective exhibition of Fairfield Porter's work was held at the Heckscher Museum in Huntington, New York, and travelled in succeeding months to the Queens Museum, New York and the Montclair Art Museum in New Jersey. The lithographic *oeuvre* was not represented in this show.

Printed by Yann Samson, the lithograph *Sun and Sea* (L. 30) was produced in 1975. *Sun and Sea* was one of the thirteen prints by thirteen artists included in a United States Bicentennial portfolio *1776 U.S.A. 1976,* commissioned and published by Special Projects Group, Chicago. The other artists represented were Richard Anuszkiewicz, Darby Bannard, Will Barnet, Romare Bearden, Ilya Bolotowsky, Janet Fish, Alan Kessler, Wendy Meng, Clayton Pond, Joseph Raffael, Deborah Remington and Barbara Sandler.

Porter also designed a poster (See Fig. XII) based on this lithograph, which was one of seven in a set of *Bicentennial Art Posters,* each of which was an adaptation of the related original lithograph in the *1776 U.S.A. 1976* portfolio.

Isle au Haut (L. 31) was Fairfield Porter's last lithograph. It was produced at the American Atelier in New York, where Porter had gone because Mauro Guiffreda was now its technical director and shop manager. Guiffreda had been the printer who proofed all of Porter's work when both were at the Bank Street Atelier. *Isle au Haut* was completed in 1975, shortly before Porter's death.

E.A. Beem wrote, "Porter often painted in a style—flat fields of luminous color—that translates nicely to lithography and it is interesting to see a painting and a print spin-off in the same room. I think that in many cases Porter was stronger as a printmaker than as a painter. This may be because the prints were generally done later in his career and so they tend to a consistency that we have no right to expect from paintings done over a lifetime."[20]

John Ashbery said that we learn from Porter's work that there are "no rules for anything, no ideas in art, just objects and materials that combine, like people, in somewhat mysterious ways. . . . In a time when art has become pathetically dependent on dictums, dogmas and manifestos, he was a fierce defender of his right not to entertain them."[21]

Paradoxically, Porter was a man of strong opinions. Whether in politics, art, or in environmental, anti-nuclear or wildlife concerns, he always had a profound consciousness of society and the human condition. The microcosms of individual lives and environs recorded in his work reflected the larger picture of a world about which he cared very much.

Porter's lithographic achievement ranks with his painted *oeuvre*. The color lithographs demonstrate painterly rather than graphic concerns; yet in translating his watercolor technique into the graphic medium, he achieved his aim of producing works with a vitality and an independent life of their own.

Joan Ludman

NOTES TO PREFACE

1. Fairfield Porter, letter to Arthur Giardelli, June 17, 1971. By permission of Mrs. Fairfield Porter.

2. Fairfield Porter, interview conducted by Paul Cummings, June 6, 1968 for the Archives of American Art/Smithsonian Institution, Washington, D.C., pages 38-39. By permission of Mrs. Fairfield Porter.

3. John Wheelwright, letter to Fairfield Porter, January 6, 1936. By permission of the Brown University Library, John Wheelwright Papers, Providence, Rhode Island.

4. Fairfield Porter, letter to John Wheelwright. Undated [1936]. Brown University Library, John Wheelwright Papers, Providence, Rhode Island. By permission of Mrs. Fairfield Porter.

5. Fairfield Porter, letter to John Wheelwright. Undated [1936]. Brown University Library, John Wheelwright Papers, Providence, Rhode Island By permission of Mrs. Fairfield Porter.

6. Fairfield Porter, letter to John Wheelwright. February 17, 1936. Brown University Library, John Wheelwright Papers, Providence, Rhode Island. By permission of Mrs. Fairfield Porter.

7. Fairfield Porter, interview with Paul Cummings, *op. cit.,* page 82.

8. Exhibition invitation, The Chicago Society of Artists, Chicago, Illinois, December 1977. By permission of the Chicago Society of Artists.

9. Philip Ferrato, introduction to *The Porter Family,* Southampton, N.Y.: The Parrish Art Museum, May 18-July 13, 1980, page 13. By permission of Philip Ferrato.

10. Fairfield Porter, interview with Paul Cummings, *op. cit.,* pages 50-51.

11. Fairfield Porter, interview with Paul Cummings, *op. cit.,* pages 50-51.

12. Ted Berrigan, letter to Joan Ludman, August 24, 1979. By permission of Ted Berrigan.

13. Fairfield Porter, quoted by John Bernard Myers in *Parenthese,* no. 3, 1975 p. 187-189. By permission of John Bernard Myers.

14. Reginald Pollack, interview with Joan Ludman, August 8, 1979.

15. Fairfield Porter, interview with Paul Cummings, *op. cit.,* pages 74-75.

16. Reginald Pollack, interview with Joan Ludman, August 8, 1979.

17. Hilton Kramer, "Fairfield Porter: Against the historical grain." *The New York Times,* February 20, 1966. Reprinted in Hilton Kramer, *The Age of the Avant-Garde: an art chronicle of 1956-1972.* New York: Farrar, Straus and Giroux, New York, 1973, pages 432-433. © 1966 by The New York Times Company. Reprinted by permission.

18. Fairfield Porter, letter to Arthur Giardelli, June 17, 1971. By permission of Mrs. Fairfield Porter.

19. Chip Elwell, letter to Joan Ludman, August 26, 1979. By permission of Chip Elwell.

20. E.A. Beem, "People and Things Connected: Fairfield Porter: Creator and Critic." *The Portland Independent* (Portland, Maine): July 27, 1979, p. 18. By permission of E.A. Beem.

21. John Ashbery, "Fairfield Porter, 1907-75," *Art in America,* vol. 64, no. 1 (January-February 1976): 20.© 1976. Reprinted by permission.

AN APPRECIATION

by David Shapiro

Fairfield Porter's work has been consistently misunderstood, neglected or underrated. The artist himself had an eerie sense of humor concerning his detachment from the centre of artistic fashion. His was the spirit of a frank de-centering, exemplified by his characteristic independence from the dogmas of abstraction or realism. When one considers his very precise engagement with the work of mechanical reproduction, or indeed, any part of his *oeuvre,* one responds to forms always informed by a wise resistance to enslavement by system.

Perhaps Porter's luminous art criticism, now emerging in *Fairfield Porter: Art in its Own Terms,* superbly edited by Rackstraw Downes, will serve as one source of illumination for the understanding and enjoyment of his art. Porter conceived his work to be an embodiment of inner and outer tension. In this, he agreed with artist-critic Adrian Stokes, who believed that the art work is a matter of reparation and of making whole. This process has much to do with the eros in Porter's work, which undergoes several stages of transformation and yet is never absent. Throughout his life, Porter praised psychoanalysis for its detailed and humble work. Thus, in Porter's prints, one feels this sense of art as a love-gift, not only in the cover illustrations for poets, but in the scenes which are homages to nature and city.

His drawing never lapsed into cliché and he drew with the freshness others attain by closing their eyes. He could keep his eyes open but always tabooed the caricature or the hint. These are investigatory shapes. In his print of *Sun and Sea,* 1975, for example, one senses his exquisite ability to render assymetrical and idiosyncratic shapes. The massive sky is divided into the repose of the larger rectangular bands; the sea and its grey waves are split into so many interesting stones. Porter was convinced that a most ambitious project was to render the sun, and I have heard his generosity toward other artists who had in his opinion come close. Here he outlined the sun in sky blue and permitted it to be a breast shape in a larger and its own sunny sky, opened up and running into the margin. Remembering Stokes, one feels that here indeed and tactfully, the concept of the "good breast" has been conjured in all its associations. For Porter, though never in a neo-Platonic sense, light was The Good, and the split sea is made into a whole by the broad corridor of light that wanders around it.

How much attention has gone into the mauve moment just above the sea? This is a print that repays the attention that Porter always invoked as the central act of art. Porter had praised Mondrian for his criticism of exactitudes, but also had felt the criticism incorporated an inherent retreat from the world. The strong Turneresque imprecisions are another form of justice and of love. On the one hand, the outlined sun is an almost diagrammatic triumph over the naturalistic stones. On the other, the particularity of waves and little margin of sand in a faint beige furnish a rebuke to all diagram. As in his cover to James Schuyler's *The Crystal*

Lithium, there is a tolerance for what might be the too-sublime outdoors, but everything is rendered as demotic, domestic and as alive as a poem of Emily Dickinson's. It is a print of tropes, of turns: the sun as an outline, a fruit, or a breast, but also as an absence; the sky as sand; the sand as sky; the whole as a fugue or a new network of interchange. Porter was a precursor of all arguments for the ecological web, and his painting is a subtle evaluation of dependency.

The prints show that Porter was not wrapped in the melodrama of archaism. His street scenes show that he found the sacred everywhere. But instead of the word sacred, one might think of what Walter Benjamin said in reference to the surrealists at their best in Nadje and in Paysan de Paris: "profane illumination." This is what is so oxymoronic about these prints of streetlamps and lumbering cabs. The city was presented as a new pastoral, as in the best sonnets of Edwin Denby and the rare photographs of Rudy Burckhardt. The Empire State Building becomes something as pink as distance itself. Lettering and neon is never disdained and the WAVERLY movie sign is an island of convention and arbitrariness. The spectator in *Sixth Avenue II* is still lured into a disjoined and difficult whole. The streetlamp with its gracefully bent neck is a little animal, but the large traffic light truly separates the composition. A single passerby shows man here to be as lopsided and lonely as anything in Porter's favorite artist, Edouard Vuillard. Man enters the city as he would a bedroom, but the bedroom is as difficult to traverse as a mountain. There is an inside-outside distortion. The traffic seems to be without passengers or drivers. The cars evoke the sense of arrested motion as in the paintings of Giorgio de Chirico. The loneliness here, however, is not a sentimental thing as in the Americana of so much of Edward Hopper. The difference might be illustrated by a linguistic analogy. Hopper emulated William Carlos Williams and a sometimes syncopated free verse with a sentimental emphasis on American speech. Porter's own artistic diction permitted all kinds of cosmopolitan allusiveness, and his every touch bears the rhetorical tradition of the impressionists and post-impressionists. His prints, therefore, are not genre offerings, particularly because they are not over-fond and they are never contemptuous. One might or might not agree with John Berger that genre begins with the display of relatively poor artifacts to propertied spectators, but at any rate Porter like Stokes had a radical mistrust of property and a radical trust in the earth.

Girl in the Woods is another success with this presentation of land and person. Here the patterning seems extreme and the earth does indeed become almost the "carpet paradigm" discussed by Joseph Masheck. The picture is filled with reticences: the stare of the girl is slightly oblique; the barn half-hidden by a rich and entangling foliage. The sweater and its ornamentation remind us that all ornament is for warmth. Cosmos and cosmetic come from one root. In this print, the world is an adornment and art here, like a sweater against grass, underlines itself. For all its reference, art in Porter accepts self-reflexiveness as one of its modes.

The prints are astonishing in their subtlety and their simplicity. The door opens on a Christmas tree. It is a conventional story about a convention. The little rocking chair and the carpet are poised before a fireplace.

How does this move us so suddenly? The whole is overlooked and tremulously penetrated. Porter's print is filled with the subjunctives that Wallace Stevens loved: if we *might* penetrate. The picture is filled with allusion to picture-making. I see the picture above the hearth or mantel and at least two other pictures on the wall. The wallpaper to the right is a grey and reticent, almost Whistlerian, interlude. The door and the hearth are broken into other rectangles. Frame within frame are pictured precisely, and the two white lamps, slightly hidden, illuminate prodigiously. When the French writer, Francis Ponge, was asked to do a text on electricity, he advertised electric light as a princess: "What nobility, what pleasure such domesticity procures!" The tree inside the house is like a little earthworks obtruding, but all the rectangles go up to make its boughs even more irregular and entrancing. No one is present, but it is a human world nevertheless.

So much has been written vulgarizing Benjamin's concept of aura. The world of printmaking is seen in that essay as destroying the sense of unicity, and Benjamin in a more or less utopian mood thinks of film as a possible way of redeeming a world deprived of uniqueness. When Porter turned his mind to printmaking, he resolved on a doubly difficult task. He was devoted to particularity and he also had shaken off simplistic dreams of the proletariatisation of art. What he tried to emphasize in his city scenes was the possible pastoral of the community seen as a pluralist palette; in his indoor scenes, the mildness of a home. We tend to depreciate the balance found here. Recent art has given us more glaring colors and more strident simplicities, but to Porter these solutions were like nuclear energy; always dangerous, inhuman technology.

In a print such as *Broadway*, with its pedestrians and its utterly non-pedestrian use of fine greys and greens, we have a witty rejoinder to all idealism in the funny streetsign:

T
Y
P
E
W
R
I
T
E
R
S
IDEAL

The rest is illegible and real, or shall we say, legibly imprecise and all too real? Porter, who loved lettering, was the least literary of printmakers. The prints are filled with a formal finesse. How fitting that Porter illustrated James Schuyler's *Hymn To Life*. His life work was a hymn to the life of art.

Columbia University, New York
Summer 1979

AN APPRECIATION

by Brooke Alexander

Fairfield Porter came late to lithography. I first thought about working with Porter in 1969. At the time, I was involved in publishing a portfolio of realist artists; I was interested in the figurative painters, or at least the ones I call "painterly realists" and regarded Fairfield as the dean of that style of painting.

I can't recall all the details of how the project began, but I remember calling John Myers, his dealer for over fifteen years, to ask if he thought Fairfield would like to do a series of four lithographs. In early May, the three of us met at the Tibor de Nagy Gallery to discuss the idea. Fairfield agreed to do the project. Clearly, he had thought about it before we met because he agreed to it immediately.

We made a visit soon afterwards to the Mourlot Studios on Barrow Street and he began to work. Fairfield had made it clear that his only experience in the medium were some black and white lithographs done in art school some thirty-five years before. As far as I know, this first lithograph was the only one for which he did not do a finished study; perhaps that is why he had so much trouble in resolving and completing it. Although it was finally editioned and signed after a great deal of work, Fairfield expressed his dissatisfaction with the print. "I can do better," he said, and asked me not to release it.

Subsequently, when he was about to make a print, he would always do a watercolor study or base the lithograph on a painting. In this manner he was able to gauge—although in each case the lithograph was quite different—how close he was to achieving his initial conception.

Several months later, he tried a second time to do some prints with Mourlot, but found working there incompatible with his temperament. I think this was largely due to his unfamiliarity with the medium and the seeming inability of the French printers to answer his questions. Since he was unable to produce anything to his satisfaction, he abandoned these efforts at the Studios. Fortunately, about this time, Fairfield had been asked by the Skowhegan School to do a lithograph for a portfolio to raise money for the school, and was beginning to work at the Bank Street Atelier. He found this shop much more to his liking and we proceeded to do our first four lithographs there.

Every few months, as if we were operating by some inner time mechanism, Fairfield would call from Southampton or stop by the gallery and say, "I want to make a lithograph." (Over the years, as I got to know Fairfield, I became used to his sudden manner: he would say what he had to say and then leave.) In any case, shortly after he had announced his intention to make a new print and the arrangements with the printers had been made, he would appear with a watercolor study and begin work. He was fond of the printers at Bank Street, particularly Jean-Pierre Rémond and Yann Samson, and would work closely with them separating the colors of the study, putting them onto plates and stones, and proofing the colors. His greatest difficulty in making lithographs was in the color proofing where one color would assume an unexpected prominence and he would have to alter the remaining colors to compensate. Very often before we would edition a lithograph, there would be no one definitive proof which would be used as a guide for the final print. Rather, he would put together what he had in mind from several proofs, taking two colors from one and other colors from the rest. Consequently, he would stand over the press during the editioning and modify the lithograph while it was being printed. He would put on an apron, mix the colors, stand by the press, and change the colors—his concentration at this stage indicated to me that this part of the lithography was what he enjoyed most. It was as if the plate-making and color-proofing were simply a warm-up for the action and tension of the actual printing.

Fairfield was a severe judge of his efforts and would express hesitancy at the success of any work, "I think it is almost what I was aiming for," he would say, when I and the printers felt it very well resolved.

To some extent, Fairfield was always experimenting with the medium. This was evident in the first group of lithographs he did where he printed two versions of *Sixth Avenue*. The color of the sky, in this case, was equally appealing in both versions so, rather than limit himself to one, he chose to print both. In *Ocean I, second state,* Fairfield eliminated one of the plates (green) from the first version and printed a small second edition. In this instance I think he was using lithography to see how little he could put on the sheet, an attempt to reduce the recognizable aspects of landscape to the least number of marks and colors, and still have the final result be both an abstraction and the scene represented.

Generally, the subjects for his lithographs came from where he lived, Southampton and Penobscot Bay in Maine. *The Table, Interior with Christmas Tree, Ocean I* are examples from Southampton; *The Dog at the Door, South Meadow, Isle au Haut* are from Maine.

Sometimes Fairfield did lithographs after paintings, and in most instances, such as *Green Girl,* the composition is similar in both the painting and print. *Isle au Haut,* his last lithograph, is an exception. He told me that there were aspects of the painting he wished to change, particularly the two children in the right foreground. So when he made the lithograph, he took them out; he felt that these figures somehow hindered the viewer from entering the painting.

While I knew generally that Fairfield liked to make prints, he rarely spoke directly about his feelings for them; we usually talked about the technical aspects of printmaking or the difficulties he was having in achieving his end. That he was a keen observer of prints and felt that they were an integral part of his artistic enterprise was revealed to me by chance. Fairfield was looking at some prints by a friend and said, "These will do a lot for your painting." I also remember a visit to his studio in Southampton which was upstairs in the barn behind the house; it was large and sparse. There was a large painting of Union Square he was working on, a portrait of his painter friend John Mac Whinnie, and all his prints together with various proofs were pinned up on the long wall. I had the feeling that they were not put up for my benefit, but that they were more or less a permanent feature in his studio. There was a book of the complete lithographs of Edouard Vuillard lying open on a chair; I had the sense that Fairfield spent hours looking at his prints with the Vuillard book at hand.

The prints were very important in Fairfield's last years, and he enjoyed traveling in from Southampton to work at Bank Street. I would stop by regularly to see how he was progressing on the proofs. During these periods of work, we would often lunch and he would usually suggest that we go to the Beatrice on West 12th Street, a restaurant that had been a favorite of his twenty years ago. We would share a bottle of wine and he would become expansive; he spoke of artists he admired, found interesting, and knew: de Kooning, Larry Rivers, Alex Katz, Red Grooms, Neil Welliver, Jane Freilicher.

For all his quiet demeanor, Fairfield was a fiercely competitive man. One January, my wife and I and our infant daughter Emily went to visit the Porters in Southampton. It was Fairfield's habit to walk his dog on the beach and he asked me to accompany him on Sunday morning. The sky was overcast, there was a stiff breeze and it was quite cold. Fairfield set a brisk pace up the beach into the wind. We were talking about the houses we passed, who lived in them in the winter, the erosion of the beach, and the like, when an icy drizzle began. Fairfield did not slacken his step and appeared not to notice our increasing wetness. From time to time, I would glance at him from the corner of my eye, hoping he would suggest that we return. He took no notice of my silent pleas and finally, at the risk of being impolite, I requested that we turn back. By this time, we were both red in the face from the driving, icy rain, and thoroughly uncomfortable. He turned without a word, but his smile told me that he had been waiting for me to give up. His competitive nature would show itself in the shop, too, when he would stand over the press and make last minute adjustments on the lithograph while it was being printed, as if challenging the printers to match his attention over the work at hand. It was all done without words or very few words, but his actions were very clear and I think he drew the best out of the printers for they enjoyed themselves hugely.

It was characteristic of his lithographs to be done in six or more colors. Often after the first two plates were printed, the work would look quite finished; then, as we printed the middle colors—three, four and five—the print would look just the opposite, quite unfinished; finally, as if by sleight of hand, as the last color or colors were printed, the lithograph would take on a quality wholly different from the earlier stages in the printing and become a realized work of art. Fairfield would smile and say, "I thought that is what would happen."

September 1979

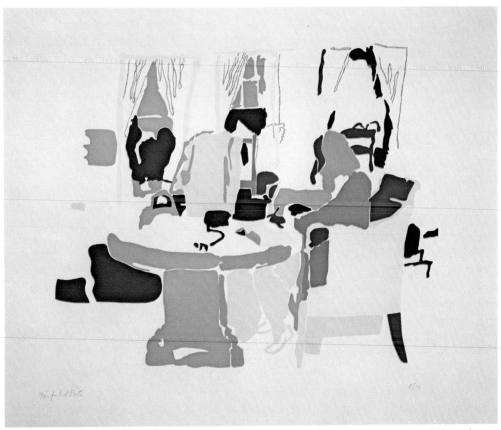

L17 Interior   Color plate 1

L19 The Dog at the Door   Color plate 2

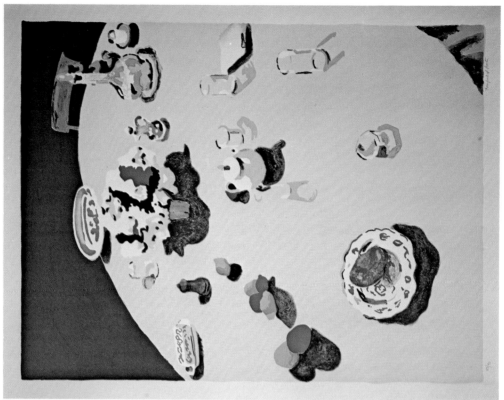

L20 The Table   Color plate 3

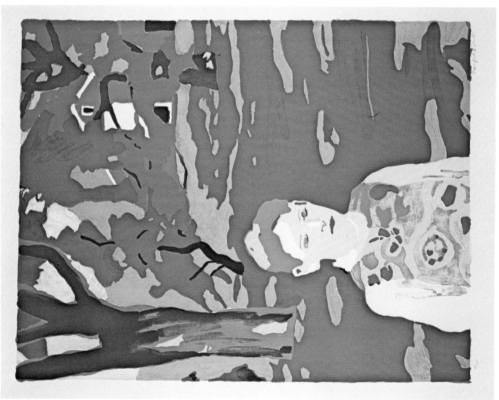

L22 Girl in the Woods   Color plate 4

L23 **Sixth Avenue I** Color plate 5

L24 **South Meadow** Color plate 6

L27 Ocean II   Color plate 7

L31 Isle au Haut   Color plate 8

AN APPRECIATION

From an interview with Jane Freilicher by Fred Deitzel

The thing that's outstanding to me about Fairfield's prints is how natural they are . . . or perhaps I should say he was a "natural" as a printmaker. He used the medium fully without getting stuck with a lot of obvious printmaking flourishes, and yet they are very diverse in feeling and subject matter. There's a kind of grace in the flow of colors lightly moving in and out . . . they don't have a "print" look, they just seem very organic. I don't think he had a preconceived, inflexible image in his mind at the start. He used whatever process he was involved in to make all the necessary distinctions and particularities of the subject in mind. He exploited a great range of technical possibilities in order to best convey the image he felt so much for.

In the lithograph *Girl in the Woods* you can recognize the face of his daughter Katharine from just a few marks because of an intensity of feeling . . . his just *willing* it to be there. In the abstractness of the last prints you feel that white sun and that water are there simply through his desire to have them there. That losing himself in the expression and flow of the work is the direct opposite of printmaking that depends on gimmickry and the use of technical effects for their own sake. For example, you point out how extraordinary the tusche work is in the later work. But what makes it extraordinary is that it is technique in the service of what was being made.

Fairfield thought of painting as something very material, that the main thing the artist is concerned with is the physical reality of his actions. His last prints are very economical in achieving effects of light . . . the way you get a sense of light on the horizon and on the water, perhaps even more effectively than in painting, where you would have to lay on the white paint. I think he got freer and freer technically, and his last work has a very broad, almost abstract quality.

Fairfield was a very . . . cultured . . . painter. He liked all kinds of painting. The influence of de Kooning had been absorbed very early. I think a major influence, as he said, was Vuillard, and Vuillard's earlier paintings are very abstract. As he became older his work became less abstract where the reverse seems to have happened with Fairfield. Maybe in the last work he came closer to achieving his ideal: those early paintings that had attracted him to Vuillard in the first place.

His subject matter of sunlight on the sea and ocean waves lent itself to an exalted, abstract look. I think that his last work was his best, which is very fortuitous for an artist, and alas, not always the case. He was able to undertake that kind of unpaintable subject, so difficult to do, because he had the confidence to attempt it. He was dealing with subject matter that is ineffable, and elusive, yet he managed to make it recognizable and interesting, and at the same time surprising. He seems to stir one's feelings about nature in a deeper way.

During the last years of his life the work seemed to go humming along. I remember seeing Fairfield at the printers when he came in from

33

Southampton in his commuting suit, carrying his attache case. He would just put on an apron, roll up his sleeves and go to work. He knew the French artisans at the presses very well by then and they enjoyed a great rapport. He spoke to them in French and there was a certain camaraderie that must have been very nice for him. I don't think I ever saw him more at ease in a social situation than when he was working around the lithograph machines. Certainly, he enjoyed making prints tremendously . . . he was really into the spirit of the work, really warmed up. I believe Fairfield thought that art ought to be a kind of inspired play, and I think you get a sense of that felicitousness as he went about his business and just kept working.

August 1979

CHRONOLOGY OF PORTER'S LIFE

1907	Born in Winnetka, Illinois on June 10th, the fourth of five children. Parents both born in Middle West: father, James Porter in Racine, Wisconsin; mother, Ruth Furness Porter in Chicago.
1913	Spends first summer and almost every summer until the year of his death at Great Spruce Head Island, Maine, purchased the year before by his father, a prosperous architect.
1919	Travels to Canada with family shortly after end of World War I.
1921	At age 14, takes first trip to Europe with his family. Sees work of Leonardo, Titian, Veronese, Turner.
1923	Admitted to Harvard at age 16; family feels he is too young. Starts a year's preparatory work at Milton Academy.
1924	Begins studies at Harvard University. In art history and the fine arts he studies with Arthur Pope and Arthur Kingsley Porter. His professor of philosophy is Alfred North Whitehead.
1927	During junior year at Harvard, contributes an illustration to humor magazine *Harvard Lampoon*. Takes summer trip to France, Germany and Russia. Sees Shchukin Collection of modern art.
1928-1930	Lives in a 15th Street boardinghouse in New York. Attends Art Students' League, studying at life classes and drawing with Boardman Robinson and Thomas Hart Benton. Meets John Marin.
1931	Travels to Italy, meets Bernard Berenson. In Rome, makes his first lithograph, an illustration for Dostoyevsky's *The Possessed*.
1932	September, marries poet Anne Channing. Settles in New York. Studies anatomy, dissecting cadavers at Cornell University School of Medicine.

1933-1936	During the period of the Great Depression becomes interested in politics and socialism.
	Teaches drawing for first time at Rebel Arts Center, a socialist club, to a class of "amateurs."
	Becomes an editor of *Arise*, a socialist counterpart of *New Masses*, in which is published his first art criticism.
	Meets radical Boston poet John Wheelwright.
	Lives for short time in Croton, New York.
1934	Son John born.
1936	Son Laurence born.
	Moves back to Winnetka when grandmother dies; lives in her house next door to his parents'.
1936-1937	Makes a series of linoleum cuts as illustrations for poems in John Wheelwright's poetry pamphlets, *Poems for a Dime* and *Poems for 2 Bits*.
1938	Sees exhibition of Vuillard and Bonnard at Art Institute of Chicago.
1938-1939	Becomes member of Chicago Society of Artists. Makes linoleum cuts as illustrations for their *Artists' Calendar*, which appear in 1939 and 1940.
1939	First one-man exhibition, at Winnetka Community House.
	Father dies. Porter and family move East again to Peekskill, New York, in the fall.
	Meets Willem de Kooning and Clement Greenberg.
	Shows in group exhibitions at Art Institute of Chicago, Philadelphia Academy, Artists' Union in Chicago.
1940	Son Jeremy born.
1943	Porter family moves to New York City. Having studied mechanical drawing before and during World War II, he is employed throughout war years by industrial designer working for United States Navy.

1945-1946 Studies at Parsons School of Design with former Louvre art restorer Jacques Maroger. Is introduced to Maroger medium.

Makes the acquaintance of the Dutch painter Van Hooten.

1949 Daughter Katharine born.

Porter family moves to Southampton, Long Island, New York.

1951 Begins exhibiting at Tibor de Nagy Gallery, New York, through recommendation of Willem de Kooning, Elaine de Kooning, Larry Rivers and Jane Freilicher.

Continues to exhibit there through 1970.

Becomes an editorial associate for *ARTnews*, remains until 1958; continues to contribute articles until 1967.

1950's Meets poets Frank O'Hara, Kenneth Koch, James Schuyler, John Ashbery. Other close friends include painters Alex Katz, Jane Wilson, Neil Welliver, Robert Dash, Paul Georges.

1956 Daughter Elizabeth born.

1959 Becomes art critic for *The Nation*. Wins Longview Foundation Award in art criticism for article on Willem de Kooning in *The Nation*.

One-man exhibition, Rhode Island School of Design, Providence.

Writes monograph *Thomas Eakins*, published by George Braziller, New York.

1959 1968 Shows work in six Whitney Museum Annuals, New York.

1960-1961 Produces a group of lithographs in a new paper-offset-plate method.

1963 One-man exhibition, University of Alabama, Tuscaloosa.

1964 Visiting artist, Skowhegan School of Painting and Sculpture, Maine.

1965 One-man exhibition, Reed College, Portland, Oregon.

1966	Lectures at Southampton College of Long Island University, New York.
	First retrospective exhibition, Cleveland Museum of Fine Arts, Ohio.
1967	One-man exhibitions, Trinity College, Hartford Connecticut; Kent State University, Kent, Ohio; Swarthmore College, Swarthmore, Pennsylvania.
	Prints a silkscreen, the only one of his career.
1968	Porter is one of ten artists selected to represent the United States at the Venice Biennale.
1969	Instructor in art at Queens College, New York.
	Dual exhibition: Fairfield Porter paintings, his brother Eliot Porter's photographs, Colby College, Waterville, Maine.
	Begins his work in color lithography.
1969-1970	Professor and artist-in-residence, Amherst College, Amherst, Massachusetts.
1970	Illustrates poem by Ted Berrigan.
1971	Completes five color lithographs.
1972	One-man exhibition, Hirschl and Adler Galleries, New York.
	One-man exhibition, Maryland Institute, College of Art, Baltimore, Maryland.
	Completes two color lithographs.
1973	Completes one color lithograph.
1974	Retrospective exhibition, Heckscher Museum, Huntington, Long Island, New York.
	One-man exhibition, Hirschl and Adler Galleries, New York.
	Visiting artist, Skowhegan School of Painting and Sculpture, Maine.
	Completes three color lithographs.

1975	Completes two color lithographs.
	September 18th dies in Southampton, Long Island, New York, age 68.
	One-man exhibition, University of Connecticut, Storrs, Connecticut.
	One-man exhibition, Brooke Alexander, Inc., New York.
1976	"Fairfield Porter: His Last Works 1974-1975," Hirschl and Adler Galleries, New York.
1977	One-man exhibition, Harbor Gallery, Cold Spring Harbor, New York.
	"Fairfield Porter's Maine," The Parrish Art Museum, Southampton, New York.
1979	One-man exhibition, Barridoff Galleries, Portland, Maine.
	"Fairfield Porter 1907-1975 Prints and Paintings," Mickelson Gallery, Washington, D.C.
1980	"The Porter Family," The Parrish Art Museum, Southampton, New York.

INTRODUCTION TO THE CATALOGUE

The printed *oeuvre* is catalogued chronologically, regardless of medium. Varying states of the same print are assigned the same Ludman number.

THE VANGUARD VERSE LINOCUTS

The linocut illustrations (L. 2–7) were not given titles by Fairfield Porter. The descriptive titles ascribed to them are in a few cases (L. 2 and 3) those used by Porter when referring to them in his letters to the poet John Wheelwright. For purposes of clarity, L. 4 through 7 have been assigned descriptive titles by the cataloguer.

Poems for A Dime and *Poems for 2 Bits,* within which the linoleum cuts appear as illustrations, are digest-size, 6¼ inches x 4½ inches, (15.8 cm. x 11.4 cm.). Some of the linocuts are full page size, and some share the page with the poems. The dimensions given, in inches and centimeters, are those of the image, height preceding width. The number of copies printed of each issue and thus the edition size of the linocuts are unknown.

Selected verses from the poems serve to clarify the subject matter of the illustrations.

THE CHICAGO SOCIETY OF ARTISTS CALENDAR PRINTS

Each of the Porter linoleum cuts in the *Artists' Calendars* is captioned with a printed title. The date listed for each is the publication year of the calendar, not the year represented within its pages.

A small number of proofs were pulled on varying kinds and sizes of papers in addition to the large limited calendar editions. The documented sheet size and type of paper refer to the individual proofs illustrated; the calendar page size and type of paper are also noted, height preceding width. Neither the proofs nor the published calendar impressions were signed or numbered.

THE BLACK AND WHITE LITHOGRAPHS

The title listed for each print is the one given it by Porter. An alternate title which appears in parentheses is supplied when record of it has been found among the Porter papers. In some cases alternate descriptive titles have been suggested by Mrs. Porter.

All the lithographs were pencil signed and numbered. An undetermined number of Artist's Proofs were so designated in pencil and signed. No publisher is listed; these lithographs were not published in the current sense, though a large group of them was purchased by and subsequently exhibited by Collectors Graphics, a division of the Peridot Gallery, New York.

THE SILKSCREEN

Each of the ten impressions of Porter's only silkscreen is signed and numbered.

THE COLOR LITHOGRAPHS

Fairfield Porter gave titles to all his color lithographs, but did not pencil title them. The two states of *Sixth Avenue* (L. 23) are pencil titled, but not in Porter's hand. In the catalogue an alternate title in parentheses is listed when record has been found of it among the Porter papers and correspondence, or in museum, gallery or dealer catalogues.

Every print is reproduced in black and white; in addition a selected and representative group of the color lithographs is repeated in color.

The colors listed in the documentation refer to the colors applied to each stone or plate; they are not descriptive of the colors as they appear in the completed print.

The date listed for each print refers to the year in which it was completed.

Dimensions are given for both paper size and image size, in inches as well as centimeters. Height precedes width. In several instances, the image occupies the full sheet. Porter used Arches paper almost exclusively, with one exception (L. 26, second state).

Edition sizes are listed; the number of Artist's Proofs printed is listed when known. In several cases, the number of Printer's Proofs pulled has been ascertained. (A Printer's Proof is signed, sometimes inscribed, and presented by the artist to the printer in appreciation for his help and workmanship. It is not part of the numbered edition.)

All the color lithographs are pencil signed and numbered. There is some evidence that unsatisfactory proofs were not always destroyed, so there may be in existence a very few off-center, off-color, unsigned proofs.

The preliminary studies for *Street Scene* (Figs. VI-X), and the sketch for *Broadway* (Fig. XI) are unsigned.

The listed *References* are arranged chronologically according to date of publication. They include books; museum collection catalogues and museum exhibition catalogues; gallery, dealer and auction catalogues; articles in periodicals and newspapers; and in a few cases, printers' and publishers' promotional materials.

Porter subscribed to the view (attributed to Alfred Frankfurter, respected former long-time editor of *Art News*) that "the best criticism is simply, the best description." The commentary accompanying each of the prints in the catalogue attempts to fulfill this criterion. Whenever possible, Fairfield Porter's own statements about his graphic work are excerpted from his writings, from his prodigious correspondence, and from his interviews. Included as well are statements from the art press, critical reviews and articles from newspapers and periodicals. Pertinent anecdotal material is provided from various sources. Each quotation is footnoted. (*F.P.* denotes Fairfield Porter; *P.C.N.* refers to *The Print Collector's Newsletter*). Full citations of sources appear in the NOTES TO THE CATALOGUE.

Porter often proclaimed in his writings and in his lectures that "Art can not be explained, it can only be experienced." The reader is invited to experience the graphic art of Fairfield Porter.

J.L.

THE CATALOGUE

CHRONOLOGICAL LIST OF THE PRINTS, ARRANGED BY MEDIUM

Ludman Number		
	BLACK AND WHITE LITHOGRAPH	
1	Illustration For *The Possessed*	c. 1931-32
	LINOLEUM CUTS	
2	Donkey and Elephant	1936
3	Three Archers	1936
4	Mining Town	1936
5	Woman Praying	1936
6	Ruins	1936
7	Irish Harp	1937
8	Annunciation, *first* and *second state*	1938
9	Street Corner	1939
10	Highway Going West	1939
	OFFSET LITHOGRAPHS	
11	Street Scene	c. 1960-61
12	Child Writing	c. 1960-61
13	Interior With Bust	c. 1960-61
14	Snow Landscape	c. 1960-61
15	House Through Window	c. 1960-61
16	Parking Lot	c. 1960-61
	SILKSCREEN	
17	Interior	1967
	COLOR LITHOGRAPHS	
18	Street Scene	1969
19	The Dog at the Door	1971
20	The Table	1971
21	The Christmas Tree	1971
22	Girl in the Woods	1971
23	Sixth Avenue *I* and *II*	1971
24	South Meadow	1972
25	Broadway	1972
26	Ocean, *first* and *second state*	1973
27	Ocean II	1974
28	Apple Blossoms I, II *and* III	1974
29	Sunrise	1974
30	Sun and Sea	1975
31	Isle Au Haut	1975

L. 1
Illustration For *The Possessed,*
By Fyodor Dostoyevsky

Medium: Black and white lithograph
Date: c. 1931–32
Sheet size: 12⅞ inches x 9¼ inches
            32.7 cm. x 23.5 cm.
Image size: 11½ inches x 8⅝ inches
            29.2 cm. x 21.9 cm.
Paper: Machine-made, buff colored, slightly glossy

"Long ago I made a lithograph in Rome, an illustration of Dostoyevsky. I thought I would illustrate *The Possessed.* I made just one illustration. I never went any further." *F.P. 1*

Among the Porter papers is a notebook written by Porter in longhand, containing a lengthy detailed summary, chapter by chapter—of Dostoyevsky's 1872 classic *The Possessed*—done in preparation for this project which never came to fruition.

". . . of all the books and poems I have read about places, those that meant most to me in this respect have been Russian novels and poems. . . . The 'places' in English literature are not nearly so real to me as those in Russian books. . . . It is, as in Russian books, very much the reality of the people for me that makes the place real. A Russian novel at its best is like one's own life; an English novel is literary." *F.P. 2*

48

L. 2
Donkey and Elephant
(Twins)

Illustration for *Masque with Clowns,* by John Brooks Wheelwright
Medium: Black and white linoleum cut
Published in *Poems for a Dime,* number 4, January 8, 1936.
Image size: 4 inches x 3 inches (10.1 cm. x 7.6 cm.)

". . . elephant in fedora and donkey in derby dancing on tables . . ."
F.P. 3

During the thirties, Porter's interest and involvement in politics
developed. This symbolic donkey and elephant, emblems of the United
States Democratic and Republican parties, was the first in a series of
Porter's linocut illustrations which appeared in various issues of *Poems for
a Dime* and *Poems for 2 Bits,* radical poetry pamphlets published from
1934 through 1937 by John Brooks Wheelwright in Boston.

In the poem *Masque with Clowns,* Wheelwright employs the device of
word-play to emphasize the poignant sarcasm of his commentary on
Depression era politics—the socialist viewpoint that both the Democrats
and Republicans were "twins" dancing to the same tune, each equally in-
effectual in the face of the problems of the Depression.

The Brown Derby brays through the maw of a Donkey, the
    Slate Fedora trumpets
through the trunk of an Elephant,
until the planks of each Platform
    crack beneath her Honky-tonky (sound
    of corks popping).
. . . Two By Gemini 1 elegant Girl Twin
    Six Day Motor
Bicycle Cyclist ORATORS (one a
    Demirep, one a *Publican*) wheeling
        in circles on armored mule *Elephant*
        and elephantine *Mule* impersonate
        the enmity
between *Brown Derby* and *Slate*
    Fedoras; one flourishing
Gold Eagles, one flashing *Silver Dollars;*
    they clog-dance
on neighboring Tables labeled:
EMANCIPATION PROCLARATION
DECLAMATION OF INDEPATION *John Wheelwright* 4

50

L. 3
Three Archers

Illustration for *Masque with Clowns,* by John Brooks Wheelwright
Medium: Black and white linoleum cut
Published in *Poems for a Dime,* number 4, January 8, 1936.
Image size: 4 inches x 3 inches (10.1 cm. x 7.6 cm.)

"I have made one linoleum cut for "Masque with Clowns" and designed three others: finished—the three archers. . . . It was much fun cutting the linoleum block." *F.P.* 5

"I like the arrows better than the twins. I think it is more artistic but less well executed perhaps. The legs of the nearest archer are not clear, but I am still baffled about how to have them more so." *F.P.* 6

The linocut of the symbolic archers, each with an arrow notched in his bowstring, is the second illustration to be inserted within the text of Wheelwright's poem *Masque with Clowns,* and is captioned:

Three arrows wing, three arrows sing,
    three arrows,
three arrows, three arrows, Arrows; Farmers
    and Millers
clad in star-spark-feathered shafts
with fore-arms flexed salute the
    Giant Archers *John Wheelwright* 7

The last verse of this paean to the workingman and his lot reads:

But the MAN makes no salute, except to strike
his handcuffs on the monstrous MACHINES:
his handcuffs spring!
Unhinged, TRACTOR and DYNAMO
disclose another WOMAN and ANOTHER MAN. *John Wheelwright* 8

Porter wrote: "I like *Masque with Clowns* except for the end . . . your way of making propaganda by going from idea to particular case in *Masque with Clowns* . . . is the way I should do it, if I could." *F.P.* 9

52

L. 4
Mining Town

Illustration for *Murder at Pottsville,* by Kenneth Whelan
Medium: Black and white linoleum cut
Published in *Poems for 2 Bits,* number 3, June 16, 1936.
Image size: 2⅛ inches x 2⅛ inches (5.4 cm. x 5.4 cm.)

Kenneth Wiggins Porter, one of the advisory editors of *Poems for a Dime* and *Poems for 2 Bits* (the *Vanguard Verse* publications of the thirties) and later a noted labor historian, describes this illustration for a poem about a tragic crime in a mining town as "an impressionistic mining-town scene . . . it does not deal with mining operations but rather with the drab sordid environment of a mining community." *Kenneth Porter* 10

Whelan's tragic and bitter poem recounts the tale of the trial of a man who has murdered his wife; and in effect, memorializes the plight of the coal miners and their families in the 1930's, ". . . that tiny mass of God's outcast humanity known as the citizens of Pottsville, Pa. . . ." *Kenneth Whelan* 11

A reporter arrives in the town to cover the trial,

Bouncing the baby Ford the
little mud spattered chariot
down around hills and corners of
snow-slushed avenues into a god-knows-where-
    I-am-town of
three thousand more or less
immortal inhabitants, where:
(EVENING EDITION: JANUARY 24)
    MAN MURDERS WIFE IN LONELY
        MINING TOWN
    POTTSVILLE, LONG CENTER OF
    STATE MINING INDUSTRY
    SCENE OF WILD MOUNTAIN TRAGEDY *Kenneth Whelan* 12

Kenneth Whelan thanked John Wheelwright in a letter of March 30, 1936 "for getting Porter to illustrate my poem." Porter states "Whelan wrote me a very nice note about the proofs: apparently he likes them!" *F.P.* 13

54

L. 5
Woman Praying

Illustration for *Murder at Pottsville,* by Kenneth Whelan
Medium: Black and white linoleum cut
Published in *Poems for 2 Bits,* number 3, June 16, 1936.
Image size: 4½ inches x 3⅛ inches (11.4 cm. x 7.9 cm.)

Porter's second linocut (see also L. 4) for Whelan's anguished and caustic poem illustrates the passage concerned with the miner O'Fallon's defense for having killed his wife:

She was too young,
I guess. The cold, the long dark hours
of these hills, sometimes no food,
no fire in the house."
(*We* understand.) "She
used to laugh though." (Smile wistfully.
Thou cracked old mask.) "I guess she
might have got along if he had lived."
(If who? The bench must know all facts.)
"The baby, born two years after. Lived
three months and died. They said it didn't
have enough.—we hadn't so
much to eat I guess—"   "The
doctor said she'd never have no more."
"I never saw a person change so (me being young)
in such a short short time. She took
to church—woke me sometimes in the
middle of the night to pray for the
soul of the baby . . ."
. . . "She hounded me. I killed her,
yes (shouting the)—I murdered
her when she had finished murdering
herself and me—murdered *Me* and *Her*—
you Hear? you Hear?—" . . . *Kenneth Whelan* 14

Poems for a dime.
number five
10ᶜ

L. 6
Ruins

Illustration for cover of *Poems for a Dime*, number 5, November 25, 1936.
Medium: Black and white linoleum cut
Image size: 4½ inches x 3¼ inches (11.4 cm. x 8.2 cm.)

"Dear Jack: Thanks for liking the cover. You are right I guess about its being too European. I couldn't find one picture from the poems in no. 5, and I kept thinking of T.S. Eliot's
> 'There the eyes are
> Sunlight on a broken column'
and of a poem by Wallace Stevens in the *Nation* called *The Men That are Falling*." F.P. 15

A very small, yet very powerful image of five sprawling human figures beneath toppling and crumbling pillars and pedestals, the linocut echoes the themes of death, decay, "end of the world" and rebirth which prevail in the poems in this issue of *Poems for a Dime*.

L. 7
Irish Harp

Illustration for *Teachers' Oath Hearing,* by Arthur Saxe
Medium: Black and white linoleum cut
Published as cover and title page of *Poems for a Dime,* number 6,
November 7, 1937.
Image size: 2½ inches x 2¼ inches (6.3 cm. x 5.7 cm.)

"Teachers' Oath Hearing by Arthur Saxe . . . has as cover decoration
(the poem is appropriately bound in heavy green paper) an amusing symbolic cut of a personified Fasces, playing on an Irish harp! One would
almost need to have lived in Boston during the 1930's, as I did, to understand this symbolism [involving] James Michael Curley, the leading Irish
Catholic politician, . . . at various times mayor of Boston and governor of
Massachusetts, . . . an ardent admirer of Benito Mussolini and his Fascist
government . . ." *Kenneth Porter* 16

Advisory editor of the *Vanguard Verse* publications Kenneth Wiggins
Porter made this comment in reference to *Irish Harp.* (A fasces is a bundle
of rods and an axe with a projecting blade, carried before Roman
magistrates as an emblem of official power.)

Saxe's ironic, satirical poem begins:

[Scene: A room in the State House, Boston, Mass., 1936. On the right,
REPRESENTATIVE HOOLIGAN, Chairman of the Hearing Committee,
flanked by its other members, beneath a large stuffed AMERICAN
EAGLE. On the left, the TEACHERS and an audience of interested par-
ties.]
REPRESENTATIVE HOOLIGAN
addresses the Teachers on the anniversary of Emerson's "Self Reliance"
Upholders, founders, watch-and-worders,
    O force behind the moral forces;
The enemy has crossed the borders
    to poison Knowledge at its sources.
You are the sheep and I the Shepherd;
    The lambs I place in your protection.
  . . .
Treason may lurk behind *belles lettres, Unum, e pluribus, et cetera.*
. . .
Watch out for radicals who meet in cellars.
Cheer the flag, buy American, tank up on beer,
And lynch anyone who wants to be freer . . . *Arthur Saxe* 17

"I liked *Teachers' Oath Hearing* very much. It is more fun than most
political poems—there should be more like it. What I admire is that when
the different groups talk they seem to say what I imagine they really feel,
not what a radical feels about them. He gets inside Rotary or the DAR or
a politician or judge and speaks the man's real embarrassing
thoughts . . ." *F.P.* 18

Irish Harp was Fairfield Porter's final contribution to the series of
rebel poetry pamphlets. With this issue, John Wheelwright ceased
publication of *Poems for a Dime* and *Poems for 2 Bits.*

60

L. 8
Annunciation, first state

Medium: Black and white linoleum cut
Date: 1938
Sheet size: 11 inches x 8½ inches
               27.9 cm. x 21.6 cm.
Image size: 7⅛ inches x 5 inches
               18.1 cm. x 12.7 cm.
Paper: Machine-made coated stock, white

Annunciation, first state, appears on the page for the week of January 22nd to the 28th, 1939 in the *Artists' Calendar* published by the Chicago Society of Artists. The calendar was printed on heavy, white paper on sheets 10¾ inches x 7¾ inches (27.1 cm. x 19.6 cm.) by Precision Press, Chicago. The "paper size" dimensions listed in the documentation above refer to the individual proof illustrated here, which was printed in addition to the large calendar edition. A small number of such proofs were pulled for each linoleum block print.

The Porter family had moved back from New York to Winnetka, Illinois in 1936 and Porter became a member of this Society, which claims the distinction of being the oldest continuously active art organization in the United States. The Chicago Society of Artists, organized in 1888, is still in existence and still active. Since 1937 it has published annually an original block-print calendar.

In 1937, the officers and directors of the Society included Ivan le Lorraine Albright, Malvin Marr Albright, and Aaron Bohrod.

The introduction to the 1939 calendar, in which *Annunciation* appears, reads: "Each week a new page—a new print—and a new view of life— depicted by a wood engraving, wood cut or linoleum cut by a member of the Chicago Society of Artists. The Society, founded in 1888, unites artists of recognized ability in fellowship and the advancement of art. Its members have exhibited in art centers throughout the world, and are represented in many public and private collections.

The first edition of these prints is limited to two thousand copies, printed from the original blocks as cut by the artists." *Artists' Calendar* 19

Annunciation, second state

Medium: Black and white linoleum cut
Date: 1938
Sheet size: 8½ inches x 6¼ inches
          21.6 cm. x 15.9 cm.
Image size: 7⅛ inches x 5 inches
          18.1 cm. x 12.7 cm
Paper: Machine-made, lightweight, white

The second state of *Annunciation* has a number of additions in the image which do not appear in the first state. The second state is initialed "F.P." in the lower left. White crosshatched lines have been added in the upper left and around the doorway, around the woman's head, beneath her knee, in the lower center of the image, and several other areas. A white bird encircled with radiating white lines (a symbol frequently used in the Renaissance tradition to denote the Holy Spirit) has been added in the doorway.

The first state of *Annunciation* was cut for the *Artists' Calendar 1939,* published by the Chicago Society of Artists. The original wood and linoleum blocks and the rights to successive prints were returned to the individual artists after the calendar was printed, but the Society retained the copyright to the calendars. Porter cut the second state when the block and the rights reverted to him.

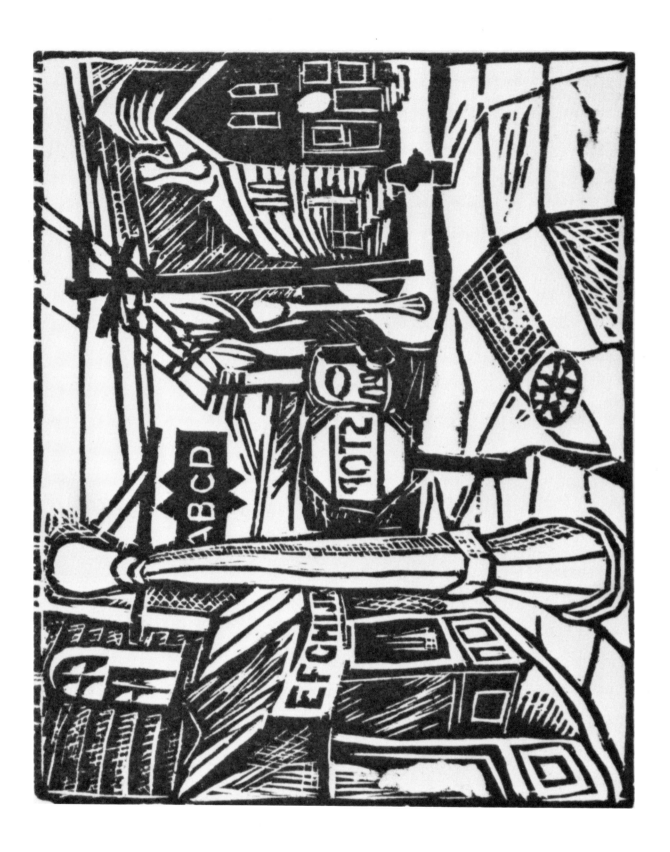

64

L. 9
Street Corner

Medium: Black and white linoleum cut
Date: 1939
Sheet size: 6¾ inches x 7¾ inches
        17.1 cm. x 19.8 cm.
Image size: 4 inches x 5 inches
        10.2 cm. x 12.7 cm.
Paper: Machine-made, lightweight, white

Street Corner was printed on the page for the week of February 25th to March 2nd in the *Artists' Calendar 1940,* published by the Chicago Society of Artists. *Highway Going West* (L. 10) also appeared in the 1940 calendar, which was printed from the artists' original blocks in an edition limited to 1,000. The calendar pages are of heavy white paper 8 inches x 10⅝ inches (20.5 cm. x 27 cm.).

A letter dated October 30, 1936, from Clara Mac Gowan, then president of the Chicago Society of Artists, to Frank Weitenkampf, then Keeper of Prints of the New York Public Library, attests to the fact that the prints in the calendars "were printed from the original wood or linoleum blocks as cut by the artists, no electros having been made," a policy which has been followed throughout the years.

Annunciation, first state (L. 8), *Street Corner* and *Highway Going West* (L. 10) comprise the group of three linocuts which Porter produced for the Chicago Society's calendars.

L. 10
Highway Going West

Medium: Black and white linoleum cut
Date: 1939
Sheet size: 7³/₄ inches x 9³/₄ inches
        19.7 cm. x 24.8 cm.
Image size: 5 inches x 7 inches
        12.7 cm. x 17.8 cm.
Paper: Machine-made, lightweight, white

The Artists' Calendar for 1940 published by the Chicago Society of Artists, pictures *Highway Going West* on the page for the week of March 3rd to March 9th. The illustrations were all printed from the artists' original blocks, in an edition limited to 1,000. Calendar size is 8 inches x 10⁵/₈ inches (20.5 cm. x 27 cm.).

The introduction to the 1940 edition of the calendar reads in part: "Here in this representative group of modern American artists in block print making may be seen the detailed, careful work of conservative artists seeking beauty in a changing world, together with dauntless crusaders filled with the unrest of the times, setting forth the most tragic aspects of life in vigorous and striking prints. Many phases of block print techniques shown here give the layman some idea of the great variety of expression possible in this fascinating medium." *Helen Forman* 20

Other members of the Chicago Society who also contributed to the Calendars of 1939 and 1940 included Emil Armin, Florence Arquin, Frances Badger, Samuel Greenburg, Carl Hoeckner, Edwin Boyd Johnson, Donald Mundt, Laura van Pappelendam and Ethel Spears.

In the fall of 1939, Fairfield Porter and his family moved back East, to Peekskill, New York. *Highway Going West* was thus his final contribution to the Chicago Society of Artists calendar series. *Annunciation, first state* (L. 8) and *Street Corner* (L. 9) were also contributed to the calendar series.

L. 11
Street Scene

Medium: Black and white offset lithograph
Date: c. 1960-61
Sheet size: 13 inches x 8⅝ inches
                33 cm. x 21.9 cm.
Image size: 12 inches x 8⅝ inches
                30.5 cm. x 21.9 cm.
Paper: Machine-made, lightweight, white
Edition: 85
Printed on the press of Jules Sherman, Drum Litho, New York

Reference: Collectors Graphics, a division of Peridot Gallery.
              Illustrated catalogue and list. New York, undated.

Street Scene is one of the group of six black and white offset lithographs done by Porter during the years 1960-61. They were done as part of an experimental program designed to test a new technique. About forty artists, many of whom were new to printmaking, participated in the program, producing approximately 140 images in varying edition sizes.

This innovative technique of producing original lithographs from a three-roller offset press, resulted in highly personalized, spontaneous prints, some simple, some more complex—"*all* full of fun and finger-prints!" The artists drew on a matrix which was a plate made of "plastic-based paper sensitive to oil crayon." *Reginald Pollack* 21

Reginald Pollack, the artist and writer, and Jules Sherman, who owned the press which was used in the printing and who funded the enterprise, organized the endeavor and taught the printmakers the process. Other artists who took part in the program along with Pollack and Porter included Jane Freilicher, Wolf Kahn, David Levine, John Heliker, Walter Murch, Nell Blaine, and Robert Goodnough.

During the period of time when this group of prints was made, Porter maintained a studio in New York City near Broadway and 20th Street. Note the shop sign on the lower right, "Offset Printing," identifying the technique used to produce this lithograph. This New York cityscape, a subject dear to Porter, is a forerunner of the later large format color lithographs *Street Scene* (L. 18), *Sixth Avenue I* and *Sixth Avenue II* (L. 23), and *Broadway* (L. 25).

70

L. 12
Child Writing
(Lizzie Drawing)

Medium: Black and white offset lithograph
Date: c. 1960-61
Sheet size: 10 inches x 14 inches
　　　　　　　25.4 cm. x 35.6 cm.
Image size. 9¼ inches x 13 inches
　　　　　　　23.5 cm. x 33 cm.
Paper: Machine-made, lightweight, white
Edition: 85
Printed on the press of Jules Sherman, Drum Litho, New York

Reference: See L. 11

　　　Reginald Pollack and Jules Sherman developed the innovative technique described on the preceding page (L. 11)—the process of producing a "true, original lithograph in its purest form by a modern method"—on high speed offset presses. *Jules Sherman 22*
　　　Child Writing is one of the six lithographs printed by Porter using this experimental paper-offset-plate method.
　　　Porter did this line portrait of his youngest daughter Elizabeth when she was about four or five years of age. She is shown drawing at a table in the front parlor of the house in Southampton, Long Island, where the family had moved in 1949.
　　　Brooke Alexander, who published Porter's later lithographs, recalls that when Porter initiated his first attempts at color lithography at the Mourlot *fils* workshop, New York, in 1969, he pulled two or three trial proofs of a print of this same subject entitled *Lizzie Drawing*, which were probably destroyed.
　　　There is an unsigned, undated oil on panel, 21 inches x 21½ inches, entitled *Lizzie Drawing*

72

L. 13
Interior With Bust

Medium: Black and white offset lithograph
Date: c. 1960-61
Sheet size: 14 inches x 10 inches
            35.6 cm. x 25.4 cm.
Image size: 13 inches x 8 inches
            33 cm. x 20.3 cm.
Paper: Machine-made, lightweight, white
Edition: 85
Printed on the press of Jules Sherman, Drum Litho, New York

Reference: See L. 11

". . . part of a large group of lithographs created by a wide range of artists working through Mr. Sherman's patronage and personal encouragement. It is my understanding that Mr. Sherman sought out artists who had never had the opportunity or inclination to work in lithography and he allowed them to use his own presses for experimentation."
Susan McTigue 23

A large and rambling white clapboard house with a wide front porch, the Porter home in Southampton, New York was built about 1840. The interior boasts fine carved moldings and rooms that are intimate and cozy and invite privacy.

This charming nook, with its busily patterned rug and wallpaper, desk, comfortable chairs, and antique lamp, is in the front room of the house. Mrs. Fairfield Porter identifies the sculptured bust as a work by Larry Rivers, a likeness of the poet-critic Frank O'Hara, which is now owned by poet John Ashbery.

Interior with Bust, the silkscreen *Interior* (L. 17), and the color lithograph *The Christmas Tree* (L. 21) epitomize Porter's intimist leanings, as in Vuillard, toward domestic imagery.

74

L. 14
Snow Landscape
(South Main Street in Winter)

Medium: Black and white offset lithograph
Date: c. 1960-61
Sheet size: 8½ inches x 13 inches
        21.6 cm. x 33 cm.
Image size: 7¾ inches x 12¾ inches
        19.7 cm. x 32.4 cm.
Paper: Machine-made, lightweight, white
Edition: 85
Printed on the press of Jules Sherman, Drum Litho, New York

Reference: See L. 11

"The result of this project is a fascinating one in which artists who had mastered other art forms were given free reign to explore lithographic techniques. While many of the prints are clearly experimental, they offer a fascinating glimpse of the artists' skill." *Susan McTigue* 24

The family home is located on this street in Southampton, Long Island. Porter wrote of the season:

"This is a beautiful and exhausting winter with endless cold weather and snow that lasts and lasts, and remains fresh and white here at least. Shovelling is exhausting . . . and sometimes the furnace goes out—in the coldest weather naturally. But everything is so much prettier than ever." *F.P.* 25

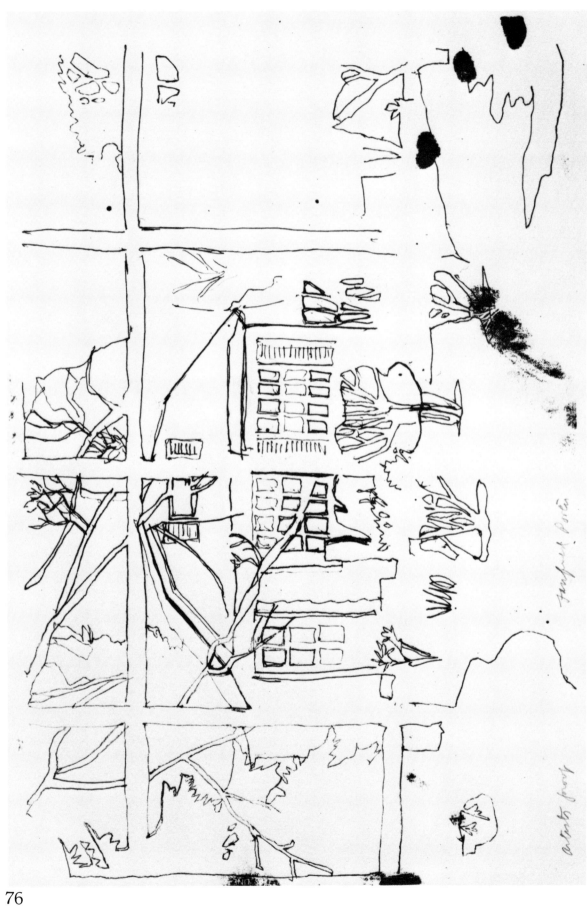

76

L. 15
House Through Window
(From the Studio Window)

Medium: Black and white offset lithograph
Date: c. 1960-61
Sheet size: 10 inches x 14 inches
                25.4 cm. x 35.6 cm.
Image size: $8\frac{1}{2}$ inches x 13 inches
                21.6 cm. x 33 cm.
Paper: Machine-made, lightweight, white
Edition: 85
Printed on the press of Jules Sherman, Drum Litho, New York

Reference: See L. 11

The three-roller offset press from which this series of prints was pulled (L. 11, 12, 13, 14, 15 and 16), produced lithographs whose images were the same as they appeared on the original matrix, *not reversed,* as is usual when pulled on a flat-bed press. According to Reginald Pollack, the developer of the paper-offset-plate technique, this feature made the process attractive to artists new to printmaking.

A hayloft in its earlier days, the spacious sloped-roof structure that served as Porter's studio in Southampton was located behind the main house. A large window and a skylight were sited to capture the north light, and the view from the studio window of the house next door was captured in this delicate line lithograph.

"If I can finish it outside I'm very glad. Sometimes I can't because there's too much light coming from all directions and the world is bigger than that. You don't know where to stop. It's hard. That's why it's easier to paint out of a window, you know, because it's something that encloses." *F.P. 26*

78

L. 16
Parking Lot
(North Main Street, Southampton)

Medium: Black and white offset lithograph
Date: c. 1960–61
Sheet size: 10 inches x 14 inches
              25.4 cm. x 35.6 cm.
Image size: 7 inches x 13 inches
              17.8 cm. x 33 cm.
Paper: Machine-made, lightweight, white
Edition: 85
Printed on the press of Jules Sherman, Drum Litho, New York

Reference: See L. 11

Half a block away from the house where he had lived the last 26 years of his life, this heavily-trafficked street was remembered by Porter as it was when it was still possible to hear roosters crowing nearby. Growing one's own food and "living on the land" were idyllic childhood memories; the encroaching city and the disappearance of farmlands deeply saddened him. Ecological problems caused by burgeoning technology, which threatened the land, man and wildlife, were always of major concern to Fairfield Porter.

Parking Lot is the last of the six experimental lithographs made with the innovative paper-offset process developed by Reginald Pollack and Jules Sherman. (See pages 69-79).

(See color plate 1)

L. 17
Interior

Medium: Nine color silkscreen
Grey, black, celadon green, sienna, red, pink, yellow-orange, yellow, dark brown

Date: 1967

Sheet size: 19⅞ inches x 23⅞ inches
50.5 cm. x 60.6 cm.

Image size: 15 inches x 18¼ inches
38.1 cm. x 46.4 cm.

Paper: Arches 88

Edition: 10

References:

Hirschl and Adler Galleries, Inc. *Recent Work by Fairfield Porter.* Introduction by Peter Schjeldahl. New York, April 11-April 29, 1972.

Harbor Gallery. *Fairfield Porter.* Cold Spring Harbor, New York, August 19-September 15, 1973.

Preston, Malcolm. "Porter without flair." *Newsday* (Garden City, N.Y.): September 11, 1973.

"*Interior,* a silkscreen, is very effective. Its color is eye-catching and its handling of an ordinary scene is visually appealing." *Malcolm Preston* 27

Porter's only silkscreen, this intimate, homey, yet mysterious *Interior* is a vignette depicting his daughter Katie sitting at a very special family table. The round table had belonged to Mrs. Porter's mother, and occupied an important place in the parlor during the time that the print was done.

The silkscreen, with its interesting ambivalence between objects and background and its compelling use of negative space was an experiment. Porter never produced another work in this medium.

Many silkscreen workshops proliferated in New York in the 1960s; it is not definitely known where *Interior* was printed. The watercolor painted preparatory to execution of the silkscreen is in the collection of the Art Institute of Chicago.

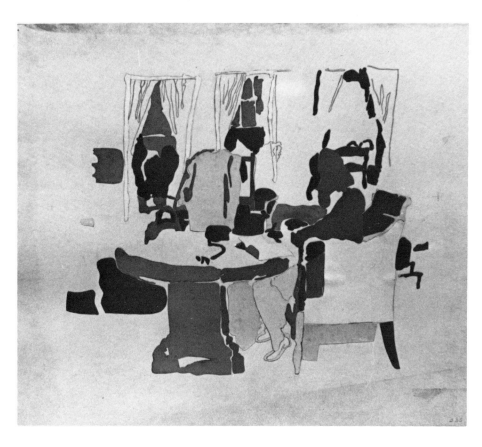

Fig. V
Collage for Interior

Date: 1967
Sheet size: 20 inches x 24 inches
            50.8 cm. x 61 cm.
Image size: 15 inches x 18¼ inches
            38.1 cm. x 46.4 cm.

   "I once made a collage to make a silkscreen. I made it by making a collage first . . . the silkscreen didn't interest me particularly." *F.P.* 28
   Cut-outs of "Color-Aid" paper (artists' papers supplied in a rich variety of hues) on manila board, in colors closely related to the finished print, were used to create the collage. The collage is not signed.

82

Fig. VI
Color drawing for *Street Scene*

Date: 1969
Sheet size: 22 inches x 27½ inches
         55.9 cm. x 69.9 cm.
Image size: 20½ inches x 22½ inches
         52.1 cm. x 57.2 cm.

When asked whether he made many drawings, Porter said; "I draw,
but they're to be for my own use for painting. Maybe that's why I
developed . . . drawing around a color because it's something to use.
That's what I want to know when I look at a drawing. I want to use it for
something that's going to be colored. So I give myself that information."
F.P. 30

Only a few of the dominant elements that emerge in the finished
print *Street Scene* are evident in this sketch on manila board. It was done
apparently to test the balance of the two dark colors on either side of the
composition.

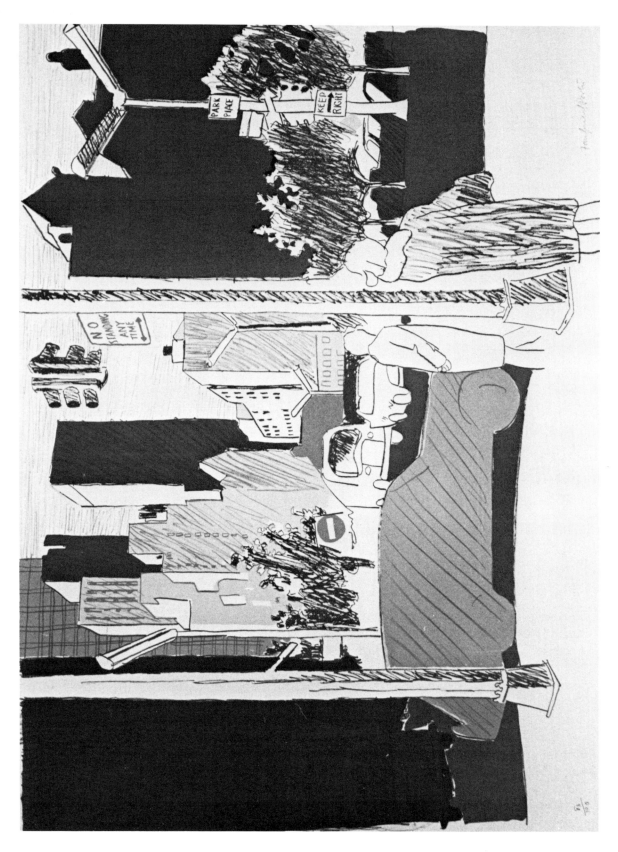

L. 18
Street Scene

Medium: Six color lithograph
　　　　Brown, blue, red, light grey, beige, dark grey
Date: 1969
Sheet size: 22¼ inches x 30 inches
　　　　56.5 cm. x 76.2 cm.
Image size: 22¼ inches x 30 inches
　　　　56.5 cm. x 76.2 cm.
Paper: Arches
Edition: 100
Printer: Mourlot Graphics, Ltd.
Publisher: Brooke Alexander, Inc., New York

Street Scene and *Lizzie Drawing* (See page 71) both printed at Mourlot Graphics, were Porter's earliest attempts at color lithography.

Porter had not been happy working at Mourlot and thereafter transferred his lithographic activities to the Bank Street Atelier (See page 19).

A preliminary sketch and early "testing" states of *Street Scene* are illustrated on the following pages. These trial proofs provide interesting insights. It is evident in this sequence of abortive attempts that Porter was trying to discover a method for translating his watercolor technique into the print medium, and trying to find ways in which to handle the darks in the composition. The print in its final signed and numbered editioned state was printed in gray outlines rather than black as in Fig X

Porter wrote: "I abandoned my lithograph, that . . . was the only possible one . . ." *F.P.* 29 Though in Porter's view the print was unsuccessful and he asked that it not be released, it holds a position of major importance in the evolution of his distinctive style in color lithography.

Fig. VII
Preliminary plate for *Street Scene*

Date: 1969
Sheet size: 23½ inches x 30 inches
          59.7 cm. x 76.2 cm.
Image size: 22 inches x 30 inches
          55.9 cm. x 76.2 cm.
Paper: Arches

    Though the tusche areas were printed, other portions of this early color study were painted in by Porter in an attempt to develop a useful technique for relating his color lithography to his watercolors.

Fig. VIII
A preliminary state of *Street Scene*

Date: 1969
Sheet size: 23½ inches x 30 inches
59.7 cm. x 76.2 cm.
Image size: 22 inches x 30 inches
55.9 cm. x 76.2 cm.
Paper: Arches

   Pulled from a different plate than the state illustrated in Fig. VII, this state, in black and white, includes additional drawing in pen and ink. In this state, as in all the studies and states shown in Figs. VI-X, Porter was, in effect, experimenting with his technical approach prior to the production of the editioned print.

Fig. IX
A preliminary state of *Street Scene*

Date: 1969
Sheet size: 23 ½ inches x 30 inches
           59.7 cm. x 76.2 cm.
Image size: 22 ¼ inches x 29 ½ inches
           56.5 cm. x 74.9 cm.
Paper: Arches

In this testing proof pulled from the same plate as Fig. VIII, the problem of what to do with the darks had still to be solved. The color areas were hand painted. There are slight changes and additions in the image: tree branches to the left of the leftmost lamppost in Fig. VIII no longer appear in Fig. IX; the lettering "DON'T WALK" is absent from the traffic sign in Fig. IX; an angled roof line has emerged above the street lights on the far right.

Fig. X
A preliminary state of *Street Scene*

Date: 1969
Sheet size: 23 1/2 inches x 30 inches
          59.7 cm. x 76.2 cm.
Image size: 22 1/4 inches x 29 3/4 inches
          56.5 cm. x 75.6 cm.
Paper: Arches

   The last state before the editioned one of *Street Scene* (L. 18) was pulled from the same plate as Fig. IX.
   The areas sketched in color and the positioning of the darks indicate that final color decisions had been made.

(See color plate 2)

L. 19
The Dog at the Door
(Boo Boo at the Door)

Medium: Seven color lithograph
Light grey, medium grey, blue, black, pink, green, yellow
Date: 1971
Sheet size: 30 inches x 22 inches
76.2 cm x 55.9 cm.
Image size: 30 inches x 22 inches
76.2 cm. x 55.9 cm.
Paper: Arches
Edition: 120; 15 Artist's Proofs
Printer: Bank Street Atelier Ltd., New York (BSA blind stamp, right
lower corner)
Publisher: Bank Street Atelier Ltd. for the benefit of the Skowhegan
School of Painting and Sculpture, Skowhegan, Maine.

References:
Ten Lithographs by Ten Artists published for the Skowhegan School. Brochure. New York: Shorewood-Bank Street Atelier, 1971.
Castleman, Riva. *Introduction* to the Portfolio "Ten Lithographs by Ten Artists." New York: Bank Street Atelier, Ltd., 1971.
"Prints and Portfolios Published," *Print Collector's Newsletter* 2, no. 4 (September-October 1971): 86-87.
Knigin, Michael and Zimiles, Murray. *The Contemporary Lithographic Workshop Around the World.* New York: Van Nostrand Reinhold, 1974.
Aldis Brown Fine Arts, Ltd. *Catalogue.* New York, 1974.
New Britain Museum of American Art. *Catalogue of the Collection.* New Britain, Connecticut, 1975.
Parrish Art Museum. *Fairfield Porter's Maine.* Introduction by Helen A. Harrison. Southampton, New York, July 2-September 11, 1977.
Sotheby Parke Bernet, Inc. *Nineteenth and Twentieth Century Prints.* New York, February 15-16, 1979.
Barridoff Galleries. *Fairfield Porter.* Essay by Rackstraw Downes. Portland, Maine, July 23-September 9, 1979.
Mickelson Gallery. *Fairfield Porter 1907-1975: Prints and Paintings.* Washington, D.C., December 3, 1979-January 28, 1980.
Oxorn, Pearl. "Fairfield Porter." *The Washington Star,* December 16, 1979. p. C2.

". . . I transferred my lithographic activities to the Bank Street Atelier, two blocks from Mourlot's, that had been in partnership with Mourlot *fils* when he first came to New York, and which helped him get established in this country. It has since lured away some of Mourlot's French technicians. It is a pleasanter place than Mourlot. It has windows, a lot of space, and a very friendly atmosphere. They don't tell you that whatever you want to do is impossible, they say, "Let's try it." I went there to make a lithograph for the benefit of Skowhegan Art School in Maine (they will pay me for it) and it turned out to be my first adequate one. It had a landscape with the caretaker's house on Great Spruce Head Island, with

continued on page 92

91

their dog on the doorsteps waiting to get in . . ." *F.P.* 31

The Dog at the Door is one of ten lithographs in the portfolio entitled "Ten Lithographs by Ten Artists." Portfolios are numbered 1/120-120/120, and ten suites, signed "Artist's Proof," were pulled on the same papers. Another set of five Artists' Proofs was also pulled.

A letter of June 5, 1970 from John Eastman, director of the Skowhegan School requesting of Porter a contribution to this portfolio published by the Bank Street Atelier for the benefit of the school, was the start of this new and highly successful period of printmaking for Porter.

The ten contributing artists, all of whom had been associated with the Skowhegan School, each received a specified sum and a set of proofs in return for the donation of a print to the portfolio. The other printmakers represented in the portfolio and their works are: Jack Beal, *Pond Lilies;* James Brooks, *The Springs;* Red Grooms, *Nervous City Street Scene;* Chaim Gross, *The Poet's Dream;* Alex Katz, *Late July;* Richard Lindner, *Redhead;* Robert Andrew Parker, *Sunday Dinner for a Soldier;* Philip Pearlstein, *Two Reclining Nudes on Rug.*

The series was printed at the Bank Street Atelier by Jean-Pierre Rémond, Michel Tabard, Mauro Giuffreda, Paul Valette, and Jeffrey Stone. It was begun in September, 1970 and completed in October, 1971. (The Bank Street Atelier Ltd. had become the Shorewood Atelier in August, 1971.)

Fairfield Porter's father was James F. Porter, an architect from Winnetka, Illinois. In the summer of 1912 he purchased Great Spruce Head Island in Penobscot Bay, Maine, as a summer retreat for his family. The island lies four miles out in the bay, and six miles by boat from the nearest town. "It was to this place that Fairfield Porter made a lifelong pilgrimage, first with his parents, brothers and sister and later with his wife, children and grandchildren." *Helen Harrison* 32

The white clapboard house shown in this lithograph is the caretaker's house, built many years before by Porter's father on Great Spruce Head Island. The dog, Boo Boo, also belonged to the caretaker, Ray Hardy. The houses in Maine were often portrayed by Porter because they were designed and built by his father. "And so in a sense if I paint that house in Maine I'm also painting a portrait of my father . . ." *F.P.* 33 There are two paintings which are strikingly similar to the lithograph: *Dog at the Door,* 1969, oil on masonite, 22 inches x 18 inches; and *Dog on the Steps,* 1971, oil on canvas, 68 inches x 54 inches. A water color was also done of this subject. (See Figs. III, IV).

"If there is a theme to this portfolio it is ten artists pursuing, as they have done at Skowhegan, their own direction. Some have taken the spirit of summer in the quiet northern countryside as an appropriate subject. Time seems suspended in Fairfield Porter's *The Dog at the Door.* Gray pervades the serene setting, providing an aura of inertia that awaits the dog's barking or the opening of the screen door." *Riva Castleman* 34

L. 20
The Table

Medium: Six color lithograph
  Pink, blue, yellow, brown, grey, orange
Date: 1971
Sheet size: 32 inches x 23½ inches
  81.3 cm. x 59.7 cm.
Image size: 28 inches x 21 inches
  71.1 cm. x 53.3 cm.
Paper: Arches
Edition: 90; 8 Artist's Proofs
Printer: Bank Street Atelier, Ltd., New York (BSA blind stamp, right
  lower margin)
Publisher: Co-published by Brooke Alexander, Inc., New York and M.
  Knoedler and Company, Inc., New York.

References:

M. Knoedler and Company, Inc. *Lithographs by de Kooning, Fairfield Porter, Paul Waldman.* New York, 1971.

"Prints and Portfolios Published." *Print Collector's Newsletter* 2, no. 2 (May-June, 1971):35.

"Prints and Portfolios Published." *Print Collector's Newsletter* 2, no. 3 (July-August, 1971): 57.

Cummings, Paul. "Fairfield Porter." *Archives of American Art Journal* 12, no. 2 (1972): 10-21.

Heckscher Museum. *Artists of Suffolk County–Part VI–Contemporary Prints.* Introduction by Ruth Solomon. Huntington, N.Y., July 16-September 3, 1972.

Brooke Alexander, Inc. *Selected Prints 1960-1977.* New York, 1977.

Goldman, Judith. Brooke Alexander: *A Decade of Print Publishing.* Boston: Boston University Art Gallery, 1978.

Barridoff Galleries. *Fairfield Porter.* Essay by Rackstraw Downes. Portland, Maine, July 23-September 3, 1979.

Beem, E.A. "People and Things Connected—Fairfield Porter: Creator and Critic". *The Portland Independent* (Portland, Maine) July 27, 1979, p. 17-19.

Mickelson Gallery. *Fairfield Porter 1907-1975: Prints and Paintings.* Washington, D.C., December 3, 1979-January 28, 1980.

Richard, Paul. "Strokes of City Light: Fairfield Porter's Window on New York." *The Washington Post* December 15, 1979. p. C 1, C 7.

Oxorn, Pearl. "Fairfield Porter." *The Washington Star* December 16, 1979. p. C 2.

"Often in still lifes—almost always in still lifes, I don't arrange them . . . usually it's just the way the dishes are on the table at the end of the meal—it strikes me suddenly. . . . That's part of my idea or my feeling about form that's interesting. It is discovered, it's the effect of something unconscious, like the dishes are in a certain arrangement at the end of a meal because people without thinking have moved things and then got up and gone away. I think it's impossible not to get some sort of form if you don't think about it. If you do think about it you can get chaos. But if you don't think about it you get form." *F.P.* 35

This is the Porter dining table after a meal at night with lemons, limes, wine and other remains of the supper which he would not allow to

93

continued on page 95

94 (See color plate 3)

be cleared or washed for the several days it took to sketch the scene!

"... My favorite piece in the show is Porter's lithograph, "The Table." It is an exquisite creation of mannerly composition which manages to remain loose. An oval table top seen from an eccentric angle set with china, it achieves vitality through the tension between imbalance and poise." *E.A. Beem* 36

"... the high angled viewpoint in "The Table" also recalls the Japanese influence." *Oxorn* 37

Work was begun on *The Table* on January 11, 1971, and completed on March 16, 1971. The artist worked directly on the one stone and five zinc plates needed for the color printing. *The Table* is one of the six lithographs pulled during 1971 at the Bank Street Atelier. These prints were Porter's first successful efforts at color lithography: *The Dog at the Door* (L. 19); *The Table* (L. 20); *The Christmas Tree* (L. 21); *Girl in the Woods* (L. 22); *Sixth Avenue I* and *Sixth Avenue II* (L. 23). All stones and plates were regrained at the end of each edition.

There are two oil on canvas versions of *The Table*, both entitled *Table at Night*, both painted in 1965 and measuring 48 inches x 34 inches, each in a private collection. There is also a related watercolor: *The Table*, 30 inches x 24 inches, in a private collection.

L. 21
The Christmas Tree
(Interior with Christmas Tree)
(Interior)

Medium: Seven color lithograph
Red, yellow, blue, black, grey, pink, brown
Date: 1971
Sheet size: 29¼ inches x 22¼ inches
74.3 cm. x 57.1 cm.
Image size: 26 inches x 20¼ inches
66 cm. x 51.4 cm.
Paper: Arches
Edition: 100; 10 Artist's Proofs
Printer: Bank Street Atelier, Ltd., New York. (BSA blind stamp, right
lower margin)
Publisher: Co-published by Brooke Alexander, Inc., New York and
M. Knoedler and Company, Inc., New York.

References:
"Prints and Portfolios Published." *Print Collector's Newsletter* 2, no. 2 (May-June 1971): 35.
Prints and Portfolios Published." *Print Collector's Newsletter* 2, no. 3 (July-August 1971): 57.
Brooke Alexander, Inc., Illustrated Print List. New York, December 1971.
M. Knoedler and Company, Inc. *Lithographs by de Kooning, Fairfield Porter, Paul Waldman.* New York, 1971.
Harbor Gallery. *Fairfield Porter.* Cold Spring Harbor, N.Y., August 19-September 15, 1973.
Preston, Malcolm. "Painters' Prints." *Newsday* (Garden City, New York). September 6, 1974.
Brooke Alexander, Inc. *Selected Prints 1960-1977.* New York 1977.
Christie's. *19th and 20th Century Prints.* New York, November 16, 1978.
Harbor Gallery. *A Selection of Great Prints.* Vol. 4. Cold Spring Harbor, N.Y., December 9, 1979-February 28, 1980.
Sotheby Parke Bernet, Inc. *Nineteenth and Twentieth Century Prints—Contemporary Prints.* New York, December 18-19, 1979.

"In *Ocean II, Interior with Christmas Tree* and *Apple Blossoms I* the splashy use of bright color, the stress on pattern and movement and the rhythms established by the interrelationship of shape, space and tone are quite handsome and appear to come more easily in the graphic technique than they do in paint. . . ." *Malcolm Preston* 38

This fireplace comes into view upon entering the Porter living room in the Southampton house. The painting shown above the mantel is an early work of Larry Rivers, who lived nearby, and whom Porter had known since 1951.

Porter's admiration for the work of Vuillard is evident in *The Christmas Tree.* He said of this artist, "What I like in Vuillard is that it seems to be ordinary, what he's doing, but the extraordinary is everywhere." *F.P.* 39

Work on *The Christmas Tree* was begun on January 11, 1971 and it was completed on March 29, 1971. It was printed from two stones and five zinc plates. It is one of the group of six lithographs (L. 19-L. 23, states I and II) "conceived and executed during the winter and spring of 1970-71 and printed at the Bank Street Atelier in New York." *Knoedler* 40

(See color plate 4)

L. 22
Girl in the Woods
(Green Girl)
(Under the Elms)

Medium: Seven color lithograph
Green, yellow-ochre, grey, blue, black, red, pink-beige
Date: 1971
Sheet size: 32¼ inches x 24½ inches
81.9 cm. x 62.2 cm.
Image size: 28½ inches x 22¼ inches
72.4 cm. x 56.5 cm.
Paper: Arches
Edition: 100; 16 Artist's Proofs and 6 Printer's Proofs
Printer: Bank Street Atelier, Ltd., New York (BSA blind stamp, right
lower margin).
Publisher: Co-published by Brooke Alexander, Inc., New York and
M. Knoedler and Company, Inc., New York

References:
"Prints and Portfolios Published." *Print Collector's Newsletter* 2, no. 2 (May-June 1971): 35.
"Prints and Portfolios Published." *Print Collector's Newsletter* 2, no. 3 (July-August 1971): 57.
Brooke Alexander, Inc. Illustrated Print List. New York, December 1971.
M. Knoedler and Company, Inc. *Lithographs by de Kooning, Fairfield Porter, Paul Waldman.* New York, 1971.
Heckscher Museum. *Artists of Suffolk County–Part VI–Contemporary Prints.* Introduction by Ruth Solomon. Huntington, N.Y., July 16-September 3, 1972.
Harbor Gallery. *Fairfield Porter.* Cold Spring Harbor, N.Y., August 19-September 15, 1973.
Preston, Malcolm. "Porter without flair." *Newsday* (Garden City, N.Y.): September 11, 1973.
Whitney Museum of American Art. *Catalogue of the Collection.* New York, 1974.
Mason Fine Prints. *Catalogue No. 21.* Glen Head, N.Y., Spring 1979.
Barridoff Galleries, *Fairfield Porter.* Essay by Rackstraw Downes. Portland, Maine, July 23-September 3, 1979.
Christie's. *19th and 20th Century Prints.* New York, September 28, 1979.
Sotheby Parke Bernet Inc. *Contemporary Art.* New York, October 19, 1979.
Harbor Gallery. *A Selection of Great Prints.* Vol. 4. Cold Spring Harbor, N.Y., December 9, 1979-February 28, 1980.
Mickelson Gallery. *Fairfield Porter 1907-1975: Prints and Paintings.* Washington, D.C., December 3, 1979-January 28, 1980.
Oxorn, Pearl. "Fairfield Porter." *The Washington Star,* December 16, 1979, p. C 2.

"Katie outdoors under the elms . . ." *F.P.* 41
". . . there is a sense of pattern and the forthright re-creation of nature and light that marked Porter as an inventive and energetic artist."
Malcolm Preston 42
"Porter had an uncommon ability to capture the ephemeral effects of light and atmosphere. Drawn to the Impressionist aesthetic, he shared

continued on page 100

with the 19th century masters a concern for overall surface patterning created by dappled light, as seen in the lithograph "Under the Elms." The cropping of forms within shallow space, which the Impressionists in turn had derived from Japanese prints, is epitomized in this work . . ."
Oxorn 43

The artist's daughter Katharine is pictured standing among patterns of dappled sunlight and shadow cast by the spreading branches of a large elm tree which grew near his Southampton studio (shown in the background). This tree played an important part in many of Porter's paintings. However, when it contracted Dutch elm disease and was cut down, Mrs. Porter recalled, it was not missed, for there was far more light in the studio!

The lithograph is strikingly similar to the oil painting *Under the Elms,* 1971-72, 62 inches x 46 inches (see Fig. XX). An original, smaller version of this painting had been stolen from a show and Porter repainted it from a photograph. There is also a watercolor of this same subject and a 24 inch by 18 inch pen and ink drawing.

Work on *Girl in the Woods* was begun on January 11, 1971 and it was completed on April 29, 1971. It was printed from seven zinc plates, and is one of the six lithographs (L. 19-23, states I and II) printed during the winter and spring of 1970-71 at the Bank Street Atelier.

L. 23
Sixth Avenue I
(Sixth Avenue, first state)

Medium: Seven color lithograph
Pink, yellow, black, light grey, blue-grey, beige, sienna
Date: 1971
Sheet size: 23 1/2 inches x 30 1/2 inches
59.7 cm. x 77.5 cm.
Image size: 21 1/4 inches x 28 1/2 inches
54 cm. x 72.4 cm.
Paper: Arches
Edition: 60, 10 Artist's Proofs and 5 Printer's Proofs
Printer: Bank Street Atelier, Ltd., New York. (BSA blind stamp, right
lower margin)
Publisher: Co-published by Brooke Alexander, Inc., New York and
M. Knoedler and Company, Inc., New York.

References:
"Prints and Portfolios Published." *Print Collector's Newsletter* 2, no. 2 (May-June 1971): 35.
"Prints and Portfolios Published." *Print Collector's Newsletter* 2, no. 3 (July-August 1971): 57.
M. Knoedler and Company, Inc. *Lithographs by de Kooning, Fairfield Porter, Paul Waldman.* New York, 1971.
Harbor Gallery. *Fairfield Porter.* Cold Spring Harbor, August 19-September 15, 1973
Whitney Museum of American Art. *Catalogue of the Collection.* New York, 1974.
Associated American Artists. *New York, New York.* Introduction by Sylvan Cole, Jr. New York, August 5-August 30, 1974.
Whitney Museum of American Art. *New York on Paper.* Introduction by Judith Goldman. New York, April 7-May 22, 1977.
Russell, John "Trapping the Look of New York." *The New York Times,* April 24, 1977, p. 25.
Christie's. *19th and 20th Century Prints.* New York, September 28, 1979.
Harbor Gallery. *A Selection of Great Prints.* Vol. 4. Cold Spring Harbor, N.Y., December 9, 1979-February 28, 1980.
Richard, Paul. "Strokes of City Light: Fairfield Porter's Window on New York." *The Washington Post,* December 15, 1979, p. C 1, C 7.

". . . A view looking north at noon on Sixth Avenue, New York, from Bleecker Street . . . in two versions, with in one, a purplish sky, and in the other, a greenish sky." *F.P. 44*

Though he did a very early street scene, the linocut of the 1930s (L. 9), and others decades later—*Street Scene* (L. 11); *Parking Lot* (L.16); *Street Scene* (L. 18)—*Sixth Avenue I* represents Porter's first successful cityscape in the medium of color lithography. He enjoyed doing urban scenes because of his love for the light of New York City. He considered the nature of the light in New York more perfect than in any city in Europe.

"Light was the great redeemer of those tumbledown houses and

101

continued on page 103

102

(See color plate 5)

many is the New York painter who has tussled with the phenomenon of New York light. Color helps, in this context: we recognize in Fairfield Porter's *Sixth Avenue* the sensation of those days in spring when the flooding in of the light from all sides at once seems almost to lift us bodily off the ground." *John Russell* 45

Work on *Sixth Avenue* was begun on April 19, 1971 and was completed on May 21, 1971. It was printed from seven zinc plates, and is one of the six lithographs produced during 1970-71 at the Bank Street Atelier, (L. 19-23, states I and II).

The two states of *Sixth Avenue* are the only prints of Porter's which are pencil titled. Jennifer Melby, production assistant at Bank Street Atelier at that time, wrote the title in the left lower margin of each impression.

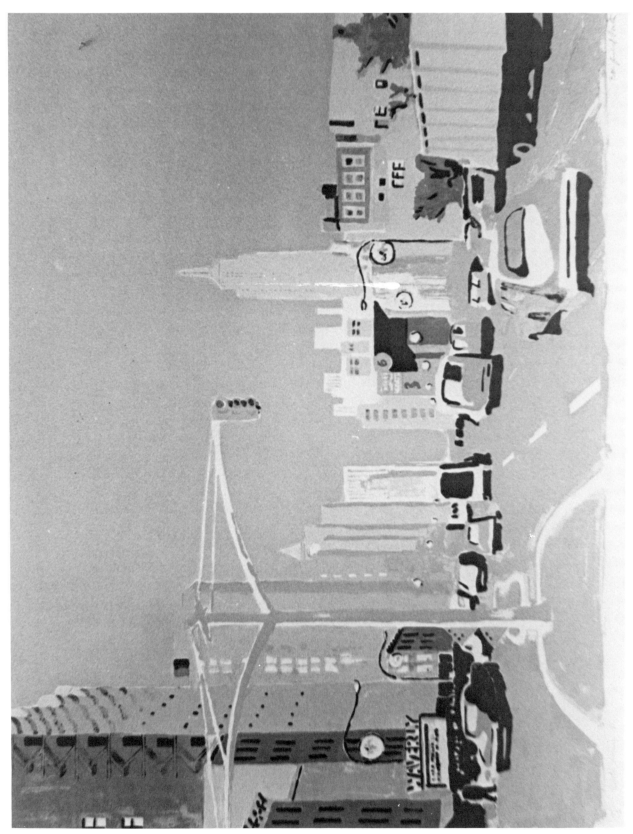

Sixth Avenue II
(Sixth Avenue, second state)

Medium: Seven color lithograph
Pink, yellow, black, light grey, blue-grey, beige, sienna
Date: 1971
Sheet size: 23½ inches x 20½ inches
59.7 cm. x 77.5 cm.
Image size: 21½ inches x 28½ inches
54 cm. x 72.4 cm.
Paper: Arches
Edition: 60; 6 Artist's Proofs
Printer: Bank Street Atelier, New York. (BSA blind stamp, right lower margin)
Publisher: Co-published by Brooke Alexander, Inc., New York and
M. Knoedler and Company, Inc., New York

References:
See *Sixth Avenue I*, page 101.
Sotheby Parke Bernet, Inc. *Nineteenth and Twentieth Century Prints*. New York, December 18-19, 1979.
Mickelson Gallery. *Fairfield Porter 1907-1975: Prints and Paintings*. Washington, D.C., December 3, 1979-January 28, 1980.

"I have finished the last lithograph that I had agreed to do, making five in all. It was a view looking up Sixth Avenue from Bleecker Street at noon. I finally made two versions, one with the sky at the bottom purplish, and one with it gray green, fading into blue. The first was most popular with everyone, but I couldn't make up my mind. I printed a small edition of each." *F.P.* 46

"Among the works . . . are two versions of a . . . lithograph both showing Sixth Avenue. One shows the early afternoon, the sky dull and overcast; the second print is much the same: the traffic has not moved, but the time seems different. Enough rose has been added to the soft gray of the sky that the picture that showed afternoon now suggests the dusk." *Richard* 47

"Rendering a scene in series at different times of day was the culminating phase of the Impressionists' activity in painting light, and Porter has extended this direction by translating the theory into the lithography medium." *Oxorn* 48

The second state of *Sixth Avenue* differs from the first state only in the slight color variation. The pale pink-purple background and pink building second from the left in the first state have become a pale yellow-green background and a light green building in the second state.

Sixth Avenue II was printed from seven zinc plates. *Sixth Avenue I* and *Sixth Avenue II* are the only prints of Porter's which are pencil titled. Jennifer Melby, production assistant of the Bank Street Atelier at that time, wrote the title in the left lower margin of each impression.

106

(See color plate 6)

L. 24
South Meadow

Medium: Seven color lithograph
　　　　　Pink, yellow, grey, light blue, blue-green, black, cobalt blue
Date: 1972
Sheet size: 23¼ inches x 32½ inches
　　　　　59.1 cm. x 82.6 cm.
Image size: 20½ inches x 30 inches
　　　　　52.1 cm. x 76.2 cm.
Paper: Arches
Edition: 75; 8 Artist's Proofs
Printer: Bank Street Atelier, Ltd., New York. (BSA blind stamp, right
　　　　　lower margin).
Publisher: Brooke Alexander, Inc., New York

References:
　　Hirschl and Adler Galleries, Inc. *Recent Work by Fairfield Porter.* Introduction by
Peter Schjeldahl. New York, April 11-April 29, 1972.
　　Brooke Alexander, Inc. *Selected Prints 1960-1977.* New York, 1977.
　　Boston University Art Gallery. *Brooke Alexander: A Decade of Print Publishing.* Text
by Judith Goldman. Boston, 1978.

　　"It is likely that Fairfield Porter felt more at home on Great Spruce
Head than anywhere else; and it is certain that he always hoped to be
able to take up permanent residence in Maine. . . . His lifelong love of
Great Spruce Head and all that the island represented to him, boy and
man, runs through his work as an undercurrent which humanizes and
subjectifies his observations. Seeing and feeling are combined by him with
consummate skill." *Helen Harrison* 49

　　The subject of the South Meadow was one which Porter returned to
again and again in his oils, watercolors and ink on paper. Fairfield's
brother Eliot Porter, the eminent photographer, writes of the South
Meadow on Great Spruce Head, in his hauntingly beautiful book *Summer
Island–Penobscot Country:* ". . . None of the berries however can equal the
wild strawberries in flavor and sweetness. They come in June and early
July and are found in their most luscious size deep in the meadow grass.
Mother was an indefatigable berry picker, and the strawberries, being
first, were the ones she most enjoyed gathering. Her favorite beds were in
the South Meadow, from where she could look down the sloping grass to
the Indian shell heaps above the beach, to the dotted rocks and small
islands beyond, and on out to the open sea. This meadow had a history of
redmen's feasts, of canoes drawn up into the grass and blazing campfires,
and later, of a white man's farm and his small sailboat anchored off shore.
. . . Mother . . . spent many hours in the meadow . . ." *Eliot Porter* 50

　　Designer-engineer Buckminster Fuller, a friend of the Porter family,
lived on Bear Island which is depicted in the upper right of the
lithograph. *South Meadow* is one of only three prints of Porter's Maine
island landscape. *The Dog at the Door* (L. 19) and *Isle au Haut* (L. 31) are
the other two.

L. 25
Broadway

Medium: Six color lithograph
        Grey, green, black, light orange, red, ivory
Date: 1972
Sheet size: 29¾ inches x 21¾ inches
        75.6 cm. x 55.2 cm.
Image size: 29¾ inches x 21¾ inches
        75.6 cm. x 55.2 cm.
Paper: Arches
Edition: 125; 10 Artist's Proofs
Printer: Bank Street Atelier, Ltd., New York. (BSA blind stamp, lower right)
Publisher: Brooke Alexander, Inc., New York

References:

Brooke Alexander Inc. Illustrated Print List. New York, October 1972.

Associated American Artists. *New York, New York*. Introduction by Sylvan Cole, Jr. New York, August 5-August 30, 1974.

Christie's. *19th and 20th Century Prints*. New York, November 16, 1978.

Barridoff Galleries. *Fairfield Porter*. Essay by Rackstraw Downes. Portland, Maine, July 23-September 3, 1979.

"I am working desperately on another city lithograph, that looks so boringly ordinary now, so unimaginative, so unlike what sometimes New York looks like in that beautiful light that is like the light in no other American or European city. I look at Bonnard's lithos of Paris in which he uses only four colors and brings out all the luminosity of streets at night in the rain, or any other time. I use color after color, and the result is no good. However sometimes Bonnard uses eight, or once even nine colors: he had trouble perhaps too." *F.P.*, 51

For years during the sixties and early seventies, Porter kept a studio in New York near Broadway and 20th Street, which is the location shown in this lithograph.

"Light is what sets me off, the quality of light in nature" *F.P.* 52 Because he loved the light in New York, Porter had a particular affinity for New York cityscapes. *Street Corner* (L. 9), *Street Scene* (L. 11), *Parking Lot* (L. 16), *Street Scene* (L. 18), *Sixth Avenue I* and *Sixth Avenue II* (L. 23), and *Broadway* (L. 25) form the largest group of prints of like subject matter in Porter's graphic *oeuvre*.

Porter also particularly enjoyed the art and technique of lettering. He gave this aspect of the composition great importance, and lettered with great care, as is evident in *Broadway*.

Broadway was the last of the eight lithographs (including both states of *Sixth Avenue*) that Fairfield Porter produced at the Bank Street Atelier (L. 19 through L. 25).

A closely related oil on canvas is also titled *Broadway*; 36 inches x 29 inches, done in 1968-71.

Fig. XI
Study for *Broadway*

Date: 1972
Sheet size: 30 inches x 22¼ inches
                76.2 cm. x 56.5 cm.
Image size: 30 inches x 22¼ inches
                76.2 cm. x 56.5 cm.

This is a preliminary gouache sketch for *Broadway* (L. 27), on Arches lavis paper. The buildings, vehicles, street standards and signs appear roughly the same as they do in the lithograph, but the figures in the lower left have evolved differently.

110

L. 26
Ocean, first state
(Ocean I)

Medium: Three color lithograph
Green, black, tan
Date: 1973
Sheet size: 22¼ inches x 30 inches
56.5 cm. x 76.2 cm.
Image size: 17¾ inches x 26½ inches
(45.1 cm. x 67.3 cm.)
Paper: Arches
Edition: 85; 9 Artist's Proofs
Printer: Resam Press, New York
Publisher: The Junior Committee of the Skowhegan School in
cooperation with Brooke Alexander, Inc., New York

References:

Brooke Alexander, Inc. and the Skowhegan School of Painting and Sculpture. Brochure. New York and Skowhegan, Maine, 1973.

Goldman, Judith. "Exploring the possibilities of the print medium." *ART news* 72, no. 7 (September 1973): 35.

"Prints and Portfolios Published." *Print Collector's Newsletter* 4, no. 4 (September-October 1973): 86.

Harbor Gallery. *Fairfield Porter.* Introduction by Claire Nicolas White. Cold Spring Harbor, New York, March 13-April 16, 1977.

The Parrish Art Museum. *Fairfield Porter's Maine.* Introduction by Helen A. Harrison. Southampton, New York, July 2-September 11, 1977.

Preston, Malcolm. "Porter in Maine." *Newsday* (Garden City, N.Y.): August 22, 1977, p. 30 A.

Worcester Art Museum. *Two Decades of American Printmaking: 1957-1977.* Worcester, Massachusetts, March 15-May 14, 1978.

Preston, Malcolm, "Down to the sea in Paintings." *Newsday* (Garden City, N.Y.): August 20, 1980, p. II 60.

". . . a lithograph of waves tackled head-on stands as a new and brave theme for this extraordinary painter of light. What strikes one is the combination of almost naive originality and sophisticated perspicacity with which he approached [this] and, especially in the lithograph, reduced them to an essence of subject matter . . ." *Claire Nicolas White* 53

"Other recent publications that also translate painterly concerns into graphic mediums include Fairfield Porter's excellent *Ocean* . . ." *Judith Goldman* 54

"Fairfield Porter's 'Ocean' . . . so simplifies, stylizes and makes bold patterns of waves and beach, as to all but lose the identifiable image of the sea. Yet in his rather abstract manner, Porter manages to capture something of the sea's rhythm, movement and form." *Malcolm Preston* 55

"A fresh and painterly view of ocean, sand and dune." *PCN* 56 This is a view of Southampton Town Beach, *not* the Maine coast. Anne Porter

continued on page 113

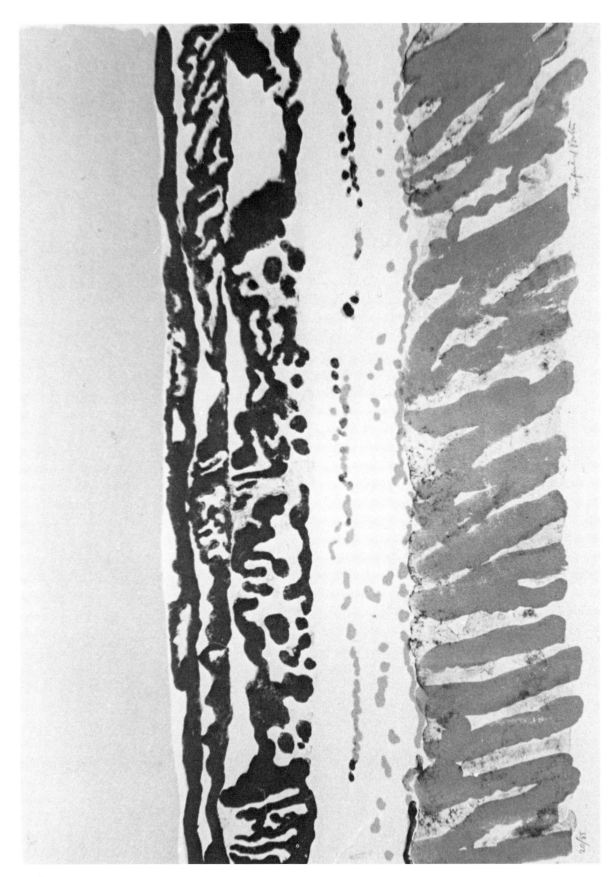

points out that the sea at their Maine island, Great Spruce Head, does not have waves. The beach there is formed by a still cove.

With his dog Bruno, a friendly golden retriever, Porter enjoyed daily brisk and vigorous early morning walks along the dunes at this beach, just a short way down the street from the house in Southampton where he had lived with his family since 1949.

Ocean was donated by Fairfield Porter, and produced and distributed by Brooke Alexander, Inc. for the benefit of the Skowhegan Scholarship Fund.

An earlier watercolor version of *Ocean* was used in the design of a book jacket for a volume of James Schuyler's poetry *The Crystal Lithium*, published by Random House, New York 1972. (See Fig. XIII, page 135).

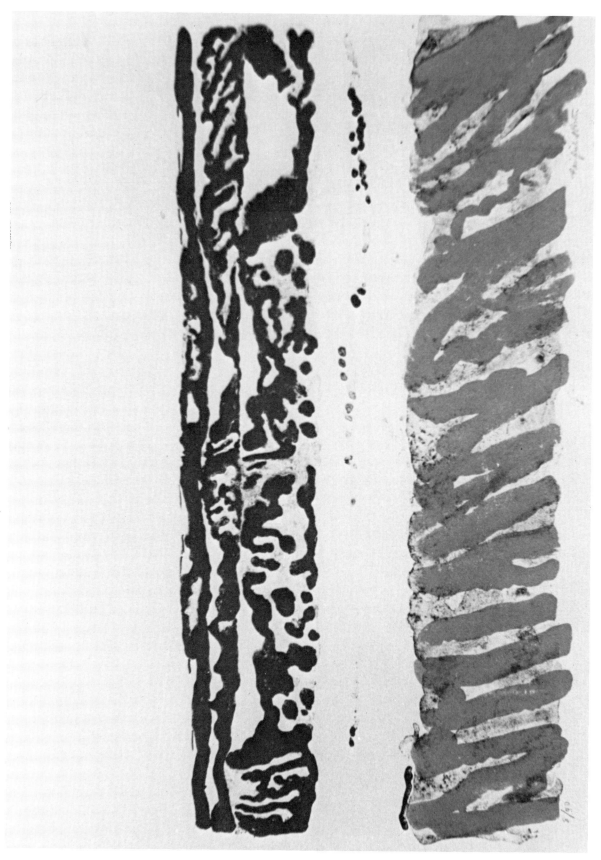

Ocean, second state
(Ocean I, second state)

Medium: Two color lithograph
Black, tan
Date: 1973
Sheet size: 23 inches x 31 inches
58.4 cm. x 78.7 cm.
Image size: 13 1/2 inches x 26 1/2 inches
34.3 cm. x 67.3 cm.
Paper: British handmade A. Millbourn paper
Edition: 40; 4 Artist's Proofs
Printer: Resam Press, New York
Publisher: Brooke Alexander, Inc., New York

References:

See *Ocean, first state* (L. 20)

Barridoff Galleries. *Fairfield Porter*. Essay by Rackstraw Downes. Portland, Maine, July 23-September 3, 1979.

"Sharper, less summery with the omission of two greens from *Ocean, first state*." PCN 57

Printed on a larger sheet and heavier paper, the only one of the color lithographs not done on Arches paper, *Ocean, second state* is a composition in two colors, black and tan—a stark and effective version of *Ocean,* first state.

116

(See color plate 7)

L. 27
Occan II
(The Gale)

Medium: Six color lithograph
　　　　　　Umber, tan, light orange, light blue, grey-green, violet-grey
Date: 1974
Sheet size: 22¼ inches x 30 inches
　　　　　　56.5 cm. x 76.2 cm.
Paper: Arches
Edition: 70; 9 Artist's Proofs
Printer: Resam Press, New York
Publisher: Brooke Alexander, Inc., New York

References:

Preston, Malcolm. "Painter's Prints." *Newsday* (Garden City, New York): September 6, 1974.

The Parrish Art Museum. *Fairfield Porter's Maine.* Introduction by Helen A. Harrison. Southampton, New York, July 2-September 11, 1977.

Preston, Malcolm. "Porter in Maine." *Newsday* (Garden City, New York): August 22, 1977, p. 30 A.

Barridoff Galleries. *Fairfield Porter.* Essay by Rackstraw Downes. Portland, Maine, July 23-September 3, 1979.

". . . picturesque details . . . give way to the spare forms and bold treatment of the . . . color lithographs, *Ocean I* and *Ocean II.*" Malcolm Preston 58

Both of these prints have been erroneously categorized as portrayals of the Maine coast. They are actually impressions of the surf at Southampton Beach, very near Porter's home, where he walked each day.

A poster issued by the William Benton Museum of the University of Connecticut for the exhibit *Selections from the Permanent Collection,* October 22-November 20, 1977, included a silkscreen translation of *Ocean II* entitled *The Gale.* (See Fig. XXI, page 142).

Evening Gale, 18 inches x 22 inches, is a closely related oil painting on masonite, done in 1973; similar also is the oil on canvas *Sudden Change of Wind,* 1973, 24 inches x 30 inches.

118

L. 28
Apple Blossoms I
(Apple Blossoms, first state)

Medium: Six color lithograph
Blue, yellow, pink, green, light green, light tan
Date: 1974
Sheet size: 23 inches x 28 inches
58.4 cm. x 71.1 cm.
Image size: 20¼ inches x 25¼ inches
51.4 cm. x 64.1 cm.
Paper: Arches
Edition: 50; 10 Artist's Proofs
Printer: Resam Press, New York
Publisher: Brooke Alexander, Inc., New York

References:

Perlmutter, Elizabeth Frank. "New Editions" in *ARTnews 73*, no. 7 (September 1974): 53.

Preston, Malcolm. "Painters' Prints." *Newsday* (Garden City, N.Y.): September 6, 1974.

Brooke Alexander, Inc. Illustrated Print List. New York, November 1974.

Barridoff Galleries. *Fairfield Porter*. Essay by Rackstraw Downes. Portland, Maine, July 23-September 3, 1979.

"Porter's latest print, *Apple Blossoms*, presents a wide green foreground and a large expanse of light blue sky. Stretching to the right across the page, large, boldly drawn apple blossoms open and tumble in bursts of beige, peach, pink, deep green and light green. Patches of bare white paper highlight the petals. The beige and brown branches are shaded with yellows and blues. Though tints overlap, blossoms, branch, and leaf abound with clear, fresh and abundant color . . ." *Elizabeth Perlmutter* 59

Apple Blossoms was done in three states with minor differences in the image and colors. The pencilled Roman numerals I, II or III appear in the left lower margin to the right of the edition numbers, identifying the state of each print. Anne Porter remembers "many trials to get the blue right!" Porter's Southampton garden is the location of this flowering apple tree, an image which appears frequently in his paintings. A work closely related to the lithograph is the 1973 watercolor *Apple Branch*, 20 inches x 25 inches, now in a private collection.

"For Fairfield Porter, the print medium permits him to continue even more effectively the use of simple, flat areas of color in exciting shapes and patterns that mark his 'new realist' paintings . . ." *Malcolm Preston* 60

120

Apple Blossoms II
(Apple Blossoms, second state)

Medium: Seven color lithograph
Blue, yellow, pink, green, light green, light tan, medium tan
Date: 1974
Sheet size: 23 inches x 28 inches
58.4 cm. x 71.1 cm.
Image size: 20¼ inches x 25¼ inches
51.4 cm. x 64.1 cm.
Paper: Arches
Edition: 50; 10 Artist's Proofs
Printer: Resam Press, New York
Publisher: Brooke Alexander, Inc., New York

References:
See *Apple Blossoms I*

A deeper tan has been added to the previously predominant white of the blossoms in this second state, and shadows of branches have emerged on the lower right.

Apple Blossoms III
(Apple Blossoms, third state)

Medium: Six color lithograph
           Blue, yellow, pink, green, light green, medium tan
Date: 1974
Sheet size: 23 inches x 28 inches
           58.4 cm. x 71.1 cm.
Image size: 20¼ inches x 25¼ inches
           51.4 cm. x 64.1 cm.
Paper: Arches
Edition: 50; 10 Artist's Proofs
Printer: Resam Press, New York
Publisher: Brooke Alexander, Inc., New York

References:
    See *Apple Blossoms I*

The deeper tan added to *Apple Blossoms II* remains, and the lighter tan which appears in both I and II has been eliminated in the third state.

124

L. 29
Sunrise

Medium: Five color lithograph
Pink, blue, grey, light blue, brown
Date: 1974
Sheet size: 35 inches x 24¾ inches
88.9 cm. x 62.9 cm.
Image size: 30 inches x 22 inches
76.2 cm. x 55.9 cm.
Paper: Arches
Edition: 50; 8 Artist's Proofs
Printer: Yann Samson, New York
Publisher: Brooke Alexander, Inc., New York

References:
Brooke Alexander, Inc. Illustrated Print List. New York, November 1974.
Barridoff Galleries. *Fairfield Porter.* Essay by Rackstraw Downes. Portland, Maine,
July 23-September 3, 1979.

Sunrise is another of Porter's impressions of the sea and sky, viewed from the vantage point of the Southampton beach near his home.

Sunrise, along with *Ocean, first* and *second states* (L.26), *Ocean II* (L. 27), and *Sun and Sea* (L. 30), form a group of lithographs of like subject matter, second in number only to the street scenes.

The quality of the light at this eastern tip of Long Island was described by Porter as a ". . . 'thin cloud sheet which the sun shines through'. . . . It seems to this writer that that thin cloud sheet with sun shining through has become a part of his inner consciousness and that it shines through into his work." *Eva Gatling 61*

Sun Rising Out of the Mist, 1973, 55 inches x 37 inches, is a closely related oil painting.

L. 30
Sun and Sea
(Blue Sunrise)

Medium: Four color lithograph
Violet, yellow-ochre, blue, grey
Date: 1975
Sheet size: 30 inches x 22¼ inches
76.2 cm. x 56.5 cm.
Image size: 26¾ inches x 19½ inches
67.9 cm. x 49.5 cm.
Paper: Arches
Edition: 75; 13 Artist's Proofs and 12 gift editions
Printer: Yann Samson, New York
Publisher: Contemporary Artists, New York, for Special Projects Group, Chicago (© FP 1975, left lower margin)

References:
Special Projects Group. *1776 U.S.A. 1976*. Chicago, Illinois, 1975.
"Prints and Portfolios Published." *Print Collector's Newsletter* 6, no. 4 (September-October, 1975): 108.
National Collection of Fine Arts, Smithsonian Institution; and Library of Congress. *Catalogue-25th National Exhibition of Prints*. Washington, D.C., May 27-September 18, 1977.
Barridoff Galleries. *Fairfield Porter*. Essay by Rackstraw Downes. Portland, Maine, July 23-September 3, 1979.

Sun and Sea was printed from one stone and 3 zinc plates.

"*1776 U.S.A. 1976* Portfolio (1975), a portfolio of 13 prints by 13 artists signed by each in an edition of 75 with 13 artist's proofs and 12 gift editions. . . . The Bicentennial portfolio, which intends to be representative of 'what's happening now' in prints, is a mixed bag indeed. Most interesting are prints by Wendy Meng and Joseph Raffael, . . . and *Sun and Sea* by print veteran Fairfield Porter." PCN 62

The other printmakers whose work is included in this portfolio are Richard Anuszkiewicz, Darby Bannard, Will Barnet, Romare Bearden, Ilya Bolotowsky, Janet Fish, Alan Kessler, Wendy Meng, Clayton Pond, Joseph Raffael, Deborah Remington and Barbara Sandler.

A poster (see Fig. XII) based on this lithograph was one of seven posters by a group of the artists listed above, included in a portfolio issued in celebration of America's Bicentennial.

Sun and Sea was chosen for inclusion in the *25th National Exhibition of Prints* held in 1977, co-sponsored by the Library of Congress and the National Collection of Fine Arts.

Sun and Sea, 30 inches x 22½ inches is a related watercolor, as is *Seascape*, a smaller watercolor, 14 inches by 11 inches. The oil on masonite *Sun and Sea*, 1974, 27 inches x 20 inches is also a painting of the same subject.

If one advances confidently in the direction of his dreams,
and endeavors to live a life which he has imagined,
he will meet with a success unexpected in common dreams.

Thoreau

BICENTENNIAL ART POSTER

128

Fig. XII
Color poster, *Sun and Sea*

Date: 1975
Sheet size: 34 inches x 26 inches
               86.4 cm. x 66 cm.
Image size: 31 ½ inches x 25 inches
               80 cm. x 63.5 cm.
Publisher: Special Projects Group, Chicago, Illinois

The poster *Sun and Sea* is based on the lithograph of the same name (L. 30). The image has been cropped at the lower border.

Of the thirteen artists who produced prints for the *1776 U.S.A. 1976* portfolio (see page 127), these seven adapted them for publication as *Bicentennial Art Posters:* Richard Anuszkiewicz, Will Barnet, Romare Bearden, Ilya Bolotowsky, Clayton Pond, Fairfield Porter and Barbara Sandler.

"Seven important contemporary American artists were commissioned to create these posters. They were given complete artistic license to interpret the Bicentennial.

The result is a remarkable fusion of American iconography: wistful, vibrant, pulsating, reminiscent of a past both disturbing and ennobling. . . . Together as a set they capture the vitality and beauty of the American spirit and of contemporary art." *Special Projects Group* 63

A "Commemorative Set" of these posters was published, printed on 20 inch x 16 inch coated 10 point board, and a portion of the proceeds from their sale was contributed to the Smithsonian Institution's Cooper-Hewitt Museum of Design in New York. Distribution of the set began in October 1975, shortly after Fairfield Porter's death.

The Henry David Thoreau quotation superimposed on the image of Porter's poster is from the Conclusion of *Walden* and reads: "If one advances confidently in the direction of his dreams, and endeavors to live a life which he has imagined, he will meet with a success unexpected in common dreams."

The production of the poster was not an enjoyable experience for Porter—it was too commercial a project; he disapproved of cropping the image and of superimposing the quotation which was not of his choosing.

97/100   Fairfield Porter

(See color plate 8)

130

L. 31
Isle au Haut

Medium: Seven color lithograph
Green, light green, grey, pink, brown, tan, black
Date: 1975
Sheet size: 28½ inches x 23¾ inches
72.4 cm. x 60.3 cm.
Image size: 25¾ inches x 22 inches
65.4 cm. x 55.9 cm.
Paper: Arches
Edition: 100; 15 Artist's Proofs
Printer: American Atelier, New York
Publisher: Brooke Alexander, Inc., New York

References:

"Prints and Portfolios Published." *Print Collector's Newsletter* 6, no. 1 (March-April 1975): 16.

Andre, Michael in "New Editions." *ARTnews* 74, no. 7 (September 1975): 56.

Brooke Alexander, Inc. *Selected Prints 1960-1977.* New York, 1977.

The Parrish Art Museum. *Fairfield Porter's Maine.* Introduction by Helen Harrison. Southampton, New York, July 2-September 11, 1977.

Goldman, Judith. *Brooke Alexander: A Decade of Print Publishing.* Boston, Mass.: Boston University Art Gallery, 1978.

Barridoff Galleries. *Fairfield Porter.* Essay by Rackstraw Downes. Portland, Maine, July 23-September 3, 1979.

"Cliffs, the sea, a tiny boat rendered with the freshness of watercolor . . ." *PCN* 64

"Fairfield Porter's *Isle au Haut,* a lithograph in transparent inks, transforms the heaving, rocky rhythms of the Isle au Haut coast of Maine into swirling line. The flat pink water contrasts with the coast, and the sky is a flat green. The green veil drops from the outline of one cloud, like tissue pulled down by something in time; such casual imperfection marks a spontaneous artist, and distinguishes Porter from the makers of clean and perfect impersonal prints who are now so commonplace." *Michael Andre* 65

The Dog at the Door (L. 19), *South Meadow* (L. 24), and *Isle au Haut* comprise the small group of lithographs Porter did of Maine through the years. His Great Spruce Head Island occupied a very special place in his heart. "I've been to Maine almost every summer since I was six. It's the place where most of all I feel myself to belong." *F.P.* 66

"For Porter, Maine was far more than a summer home. He saw it not only with the nostalgic eye of a seasonal resident, but also with an artist's keen awareness. The clarity and purity of the light, the interplay of land and water and the temperate lushness of the coastal scenery are all evident in his work. . . . When we see the Maine coast through Porter's eyes, we see first of all works of visual art derived from . . . aesthetic

continued on page 132

vision . . . and technical ability . . . but we also see Porter's attitude toward a special landscape . . ." *Helen Harrison* 67

The lithograph *Isle au Haut* was made after Porter's oil on canvas *Cliffs of Isle au Haut* (72 inches x 62 inches). The painting was done during the summer of 1974 for inclusion in the travelling exhibition commissioned and sponsored by the United States Department of the Interior in celebration of the 1976 Bicentennial. There are also two related watercolors entitled *Isle au Haut*.

One summer several years before, Porter had written: "Going to Maine always excites me as much as going to Europe. It has all kinds of emotions attached to it for me: the island stands for my personal golden age (my childhood) and in addition it is very beautiful . . . The melancholy feelings are partly personal and partly a response to something actually melancholy and beautiful, a gain and loss at once . . ." *F.P.* 68

Upon leaving the island at the end of another summer, Porter had written a poem *The Wave and the Leaf* which reads in part:

"I am here alone, as if on retreat,
Alone with the melancholy that is inherent to the beauty of the island.
Sorrow lies down on the rocks
Like a thin soil
It is the watery medium of the multiplicity of events . . ."

F.P. 69

Isle au Haut was the last print Fairfield Porter made before his death in September, 1975.

APPENDIX I: Bookjackets

"Did you know that I had done some bookjackets for friends' poems, which I have enjoyed doing. I like to feel that I can do commercial art too . . ." *F.P. 70*

Fig. XIII
The Crystal Lithium
poems by James Schuyler
New York: Random House, Inc., 1972
Painting by Fairfield Porter. Bookjacket, in colors, printed September 1972.

Fig. XIV
Rose, where did you get that red?
Teaching Great Poetry to Children
by Kenneth Koch
New York: Random House, Inc., 1973.
Jacket illustration and design by Fairfield Porter. Bookjacket, in colors,
printed September 1973.

Fig. XV
Hymn to Life
poems by James Schuyler
New York: Random House, Inc., 1974
Jacket design by Fairfield Porter. Bookjacket, in colors, printed March 1974.

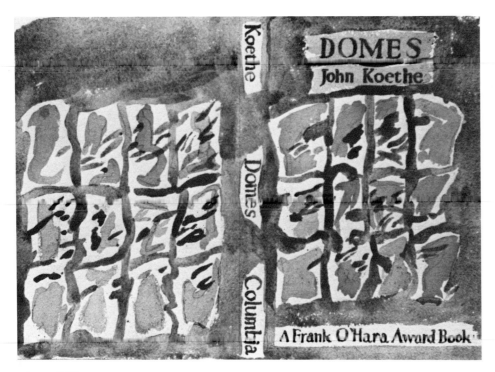

Fig. XVI
Domes

by John Koethe—A Frank O'Hara Award Book
New York: Columbia University Press, 1972.
Jacket design by Fairfield Porter.

This is the original watercolor used in the final bookjacket design for
Domes.

APPENDIX II

Scorpion, Eagle and Dove (A Love Poem)
by Ted Berrigan, 1970.

Fig. XVII

Illustrated with black and white drawing by Fairfield Porter. Lettered by, and plate inked by Fairfield Porter. Zinc plate made by Robert Keene, Southampton, New York; printed on his platen press (Chandler-Price press, a now obsolete electrolysis process). Printed in December 1970 in an edition of 150, on sheet of paper 17 inches x 11 inches (43.2 cm. x 27.9 cm.); image size 14¾ inches x 9⅞ inches (37.5 cm. x 25.1 cm.); 45 impressions were signed by both Porter and Berrigan.

APPENDIX III

Fig. XVIII
Poster, in black and white, published by the Tibor de Nagy Gallery, New York, in 1970. Poster size: 23¾ inches x 13¾ inches (61 cm. x 35 cm.).

The illustration is of the liquitex and casein on canvas *The Porch Door*, 1962. Image size on poster: 17 inches x 13¾ inches (43 cm. x 35 cm.).

APPENDIX IV

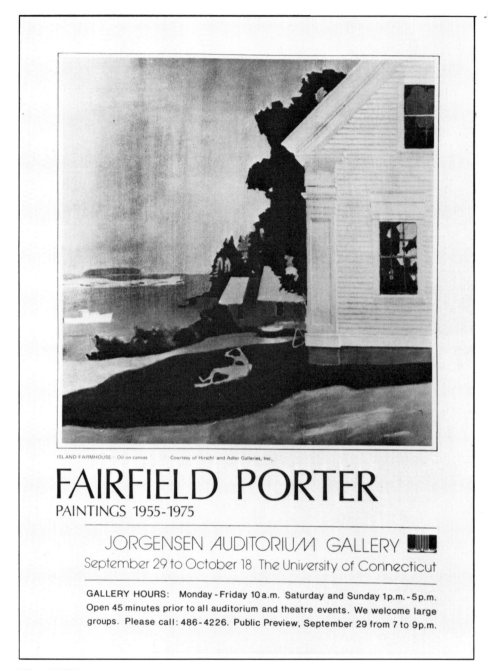

ISLAND FARMHOUSE Oil on canvas   Courtesy of Hirschl and Adler Galleries, Inc.

FAIRFIELD PORTER
PAINTINGS 1955-1975

JORGENSEN AUDITORIUM GALLERY
September 29 to October 18 The University of Connecticut

GALLERY HOURS: Monday - Friday 10 a.m. Saturday and Sunday 1 p.m. - 5 p.m.
Open 45 minutes prior to all auditorium and theatre events. We welcome large
groups. Please call: 486-4226. Public Preview, September 29 from 7 to 9 p.m.

Fig. XIX
Poster, in black and white, published by the Jorgensen Gallery, University of Connecticut, Storrs, in 1975. Poster size: 14 inches x 10 inches (35.6 cm. x 25.4 cm.).

The illustration is of the oil on canvas *Island Farmhouse*. Image size on poster: 8 1/8 inches x 7 7/8 inches (20.7 cm. x 20 cm.).

The poster was designed by Robert Neff.

The exhibition was held shortly after Porter's death.

APPENDIX V

Fig. XX

Poster, in brown and white, issued by David Hamilton Gallery, Charleston, South Carolina and Tatistcheff and Company, Inc., New York during the first Spoleto U.S.A. Festival in Charleston, 1977. Poster size: 20⅛ inches x 14⅛ inches (51.1 cm. x 35.9 cm.).

The illustration is of the oil on canvas *Under the Elms* (see page 100). Image size on poster: 12¼ inches x 9 inches (31.1 cm. x 22.9 cm.).

The poster was designed by Manning Williams and David Hamilton. This Spoleto Festival was held almost two years after Porter's death.

APPENDIX VI

Silk screen translation of *The Gale*, lithograph by Fairfield Porter. 22⅞″ x 30″

SELECTIONS FROM THE PERMANENT COLLECTION

Charles Olson's Gloucester: Photographs by Lynn Swigart

Southwestern Pottery from Dartmouth College

October 22 - November 20, 1977
Monday - Saturday 10:00-4:30
Sunday 1:00-5:00

THE WILLIAM BENTON MUSEUM OF ART
THE UNIVERSITY OF CONNECTICUT, STORRS

Fig. XXI
Color Poster published by The William Benton Museum of Art, The
University of Connecticut, Storrs, in 1977. Poster size: 26 inches x
20 inches (66 cm. x 50.8 cm.).

The illustration is a silkscreen translation of *Ocean II* (L. 27). Image
size on poster: 14½ inches x 18½ inches (36.8 cm. x 47 cm.).

This show was held a few years after Porter's death.

142

NOTES TO THE CATALOGUE

1. Fairfield Porter, interview conducted by Paul Cummings, June 6, 1968 for the Archives of American Art/Smithsonian Institution, Washington, D.C. page 75. By permission of Mrs. Fairfield Porter.

2. Fairfield Porter, quoted in Alan Gussow, *A Sense of Place* (San Francisco/New York: Friends of the Earth, Seabury Press, 1971) page 145. Quotation from Fairfield Porter used by courtesy of Friends of the Earth.

3. Fairfield Porter, letter to John Wheelwright, undated [1935]. Brown University Library, John Wheelwright Papers. By permission of Mrs. Fairfield Porter.

4. John Brooks Wheelwright, "Masque with Clowns," *Poems for a Dime*, No. 4 (January 8, 1936). John Brooks Wheelwright, *Collected Poems*, Alvin H. Rosenfeld, ed. All Rights Reserved. Copyright © 1971 by Louise Wheelwright Damon. Reprinted by permission of New Directions.

5. Fairfield Porter, letter to John Wheelwright, undated [1935]. Brown University Library, John Wheelwright Papers. By permission of Mrs. Fairfield Porter.

6. Fairfield Porter, letter to John Wheelwright undated [1936]. Brown University Library, John Wheelwright Papers. By permission of Mrs. Fairfield Porter.

7. John Brooks Wheelwright, "Masque with Clowns," *op. cit.*

8. *Ibid.*

9. Fairfield Porter, letter to John Wheelwright, undated [1936]. Brown University Library, John Wheelwright Papers. By permission of Mrs. Fairfield Porter.

10. Kenneth Wiggins Porter, Professor Emeritus of History, University of Oregon, Eugene, Ore., letters to Joan Ludman, May 11, 1979 and July 5, 1979. By permission of Kenneth W. Porter.

11. Kenneth Whelan, "Murder at Pottsville," in *Poems for 2 Bits*, no. 3 (June 16, 1936). By permission of Kenneth E. Whelan.

12. *Ibid.* By permission of Kenneth E. Whelan.

13. Fairfield Porter, letter to John Wheelwright, undated [1936]. Brown University Library, John Wheelwright Papers. By permission of Mrs. Fairfield Porter.

14. Kenneth Whelan, *op. cit.* By permission of Kenneth E. Whelan.

15. Fairfield Porter, letter to John Wheelwright, undated [1936]. Brown University Library, John Wheelwright Papers. By permission of Mrs. Fairfield Porter.

16. Kenneth Wiggins Porter, letter to Joan Ludman, May 11, 1979. By permission of Kenneth Porter.

17. Arthur Saxe, "Teachers' Oath Hearing," in *Poems for a Dime*, no. 6 (November 7, 1937).

18. Fairfield Porter, letter to John Wheelwright, undated [1937]. Brown University Library, John Wheelwright Papers. By permission of Mrs. Fairfield Porter.

19. *Artists' Calendar 1939* Chicago: Chicago Society of Artists, 1939. By permission of the Chicago Society of Artists.

20. Helen Forman, *Artists' Calendar 1940* Chicago: Chicago Society of Artists, 1939. By permission of the Chicago Society of Artists.

21. Reginald Pollack, interview with author, July 30, 1979.

22. Jules Sherman, interview with author, February 21, 1979.

23. Susan McTigue, assistant to the Director, Neuberger Museum, Purchase, New York; letter to the author, May 3, 1979. By permission of Susan McTigue.

24. Susan McTigue, assistant to the Director, Neuberger Museum, Purchase, New York; letter to the author, May 3, 1979. By permission of Susan McTigue.

25. Fairfield Porter, letter to Howard Griffin, January 28, 1961. By permission of Mrs. Fairfield Porter.

26. Fairfield Porter, as told to Paul Cummings, *op. cit.*, page 82. By permission of Mrs. Fairfield Porter.

27. Malcolm Preston, "Porter without flair." *Newsday* (Garden City, N.Y.): September 11, 1973. By permission of Malcolm Preston, Art Critic, *Newsday*.

28. Fairfield Porter, as told to Paul Cummings, *op. cit.*, page 74. By permission of Mrs. Fairfield Porter.

29. Fairfield Porter, letter to Arthur Giardelli, June 17, 1971. By permission of Mrs. Fairfield Porter.

30. Fairfield Porter, as told to Paul Cummings, *op. cit.*, page 75. By permission of Mrs. Fairfield Porter.

31. Fairfield Porter, letter to Arthur Giardelli, June 17, 1971. By permission of Mrs. Fairfield Porter.

32. Helen A. Harrison, *Fairfield Porter's Maine* (Southampton, N.Y.; Parrish Art Museum, 1977). By permission of Helen A. Harrison and the Parrish Art Museum.

33. Fairfield Porter, as told to Paul Cummings, *op. cit.*, page 83. By permission of Mrs. Fairfield Porter.

34. Riva Castleman, *Introduction* to the portfolio "Ten Lithographs by Ten Artists." New York: Bank Street Atelier, Ltd., 1971. By permission of Riva Castleman.

35. Fairfield Porter, interview conducted by Paul Cummings, June 6, 1968 for the Archives of American Art/Smithsonian Institution, Washington, D.C.; in *Archives of American Art Journal* 12, no. 2 (1972): 20-21. By permission of Mrs. Fairfield Porter.

36. E.A. Beem, "People and Things Connected—Fairfield Porter: Creator and Critic." *The Portland Independent* (Portland, Maine): July 27, 1979, page 19. By permission of E.A. Beem.

37. Pearl Oxorn, "Fairfield Porter." *The Washington Star* (Washington, D.C.): December 16, 1979, page C 2. Used by permission.

38. Malcolm Preston, "Painters' Prints." *Newsday* (Garden City, N.Y.): September 6, 1974. By permission of Malcolm Preston, Art Critic, *Newsday*.

39. Fairfield Porter, interview conducted by Paul Cummings, June 6, 1968 for the Archives of American Art/Smithsonian Institution, Washington, D.C. page 82. By permission of Mrs. Fairfield Porter.

40. M. Knoedler and Company, Inc. *Lithographs by de Kooning, Fairfield Porter, Paul Waldman*, New York, 1971.

41. Fairfield Porter, letter to Arthur Giardelli, June 17, 1971. By permission of Mrs. Fairfield Porter.

42. Malcolm Preston, "Porter without flair." *Newsday* (Garden City, N.Y.): September 11, 1973. By permission of Malcolm Preston, Art Critic, *Newsday*.

43. Pearl Oxorn, "Fairfield Porter." *The Washington Star* (Washington, D.C.): December 16, 1979, page C 2. Used by permission.

44. Fairfield Porter, letter to Arthur Giardelli, June 17, 1971. By permission of Mrs. Fairfield Porter.

45. John Russell, "Trapping the look of New York," *The New York Times*, April 24, 1977, page 25. • 1977 by The New York Times Company. Reprinted by permission.

46. Fairfield Porter, letter to Lucien Day, May 27, 1971. By permission of Mrs. Fairfield Porter.

47. Paul Richard, "Strokes of City Light: Fairfield Porter's Window on New York." *The Washington Post* (Washington, D.C.): December 15, 1979, page C 7. Used by permission.

48. Pearl Oxorn, "Fairfield Porter." *The Washington Star* (Washington, D.C.): December 16, 1979, page C 2. Used by permission.

49. Helen A. Harrison *Fairfield Porter's Maine*. Southampton, New York: The Parrish Art Museum, July 2-September 11, 1977. By permission of Helen A. Harrison and The Parrish Art Museum.

50. Eliot Porter, *Summer Island, Penobscot Country*. San Francisco/New York: Sierra Club/Ballantine Books, 1966, 1976, page 46. Used by permission.

51. Fairfield Porter, letter to Ron Padgett, February 4, 1972. By permission of Mrs. Fairfield Porter.

52. Fairfield Porter, quoted in Alan Gussow, *A Sense of Place*. (San Francisco/New York: Friends of the Earth/Seabury Press, 1971): page 145. Quotation from Fairfield Porter used by courtesy of Friends of the Earth.

53. Claire Nicolas White, *Fairfield Porter*, Cold Spring Harbor, New York: Harbor Gallery, March 13-April 16, 1977. By permission of Claire Nicolas White.

54. Judith Goldman, "Exploring the possibilities of the print medium," *ARTnews 72*, no. 7 (September 1973): 35. Reprinted by permission of *ARTnews*. © ARTnews Associates, 122 E. 42nd Street, New York, New York 10017.

55. Malcolm Preston, "Down to the sea in Paintings," *Newsday* (Garden City, N.Y.): August 20, 1980, page II 60. By permission of Malcolm Preston, Art Critic, *Newsday*.

56. "Prints and Portfolios Published," *Print Collector's Newsletter* 4, no. 4 (September-October 1973): 86. Reprinted by permission of *Print Collector's Newsletter*.

57. "Prints and Portfolios Published," *Print Collector's Newsletter* 4, no. 4 (September-October 1973): 86. Reprinted by permission of *Print Collector's Newsletter*.

58. Malcolm Preston, "Porter in Maine," *Newsday* (Garden City, N.Y.): August 22, 1977, page 30 A. By permission of Malcolm Preston, Art Critic, *Newsday*.

59. Elizabeth Frank Perlmutter, "New Editions" in *ARTnews* 73, no. 7 (September 1974): 53. Reprinted by permission of *ARTnews*. © ARTnews Associates, 122 E. 42nd Street, New York, New York 10017.

60. Malcolm Preston, "Painters' Prints" *Newsday* (Garden City, New York): September 6, 1974. By permission of Malcolm Preston, Art Critic, *Newsday*.

61. Eva Ingersoll Gatling, *Fairfield Porter Retrospective Exhibition.* Huntington, New York: The Heckscher Museum, December 15, 1974-January 26, 1975, page 6. By permission of The Heckscher Museum.

62. "Prints and Portfolios Published," *Print Collector's Newsletter* 6, no. 4 (September-October 1975): 108. Reprinted by permission of *Print Collector's Newsletter*.

63. Special Projects Group, Promotional advertisement, October 1975, appeared in *New York* magazine, October 13, 1975. Reprinted by permission.

64. "Prints and Portfolios Published," *Print Collector's Newsletter* 6, no. 1 (March-April 1975): 16. Reprinted by permission of *Print Collector's Newsletter*.

65. Michael Andre, in "New Editions," *ARTnews* 74, no. 7 (September 1975): 56. Reprinted by permission of *ARTnews*. © ARTnews Associates, 122 E. 42nd Street, New York, New York 10017.

66. Fairfield Porter, quoted in *Fairfield Porter's Maine.* Introduction by Helen A. Harrison. Southampton, New York: The Parrish Art Museum, July 2-September 11, 1977.

67. Helen A. Harrison, *Fairfield Porter's Maine.* Southampton, New York: The Parrish Art Museum, July 2-September 11, 1977. By permission of Helen A. Harrison and The Parrish Art Museum.

68. Fairfield Porter, letter to Howard Griffin, June 20, 1961. By permission of Mrs. Fairfield Porter.

69. Fairfield Porter, *The Wave and the Leaf,* in James Schuyler's anthology *49 South* n.d. By permission of Mrs. Fairfield Porter.

70. Fairfield Porter, letter to Howard Griffin, August 14, 1974. By permission of Mrs. Fairfield Porter.

PHOTOGRAPHIC CREDITS

Courtesy of Brooke Alexander, Inc., New York: L. 11; 12; 13; 14; 15; 18; 19; 21; 22; 23, first and second states; 24; 25; 26, first and second states; 27; 28, first, second and third states; 29; 30; 31. Photography by Eric Pollitzer.

Courtesy of Columbia University Press, New York: Fig. XVI. Photography by Eric Pollitzer.

Courtesy of *Harvard Lampoon,* Cambridge, Massachusetts, and General Research and Humanities Division, The New York Public Library, Astor, Lenox and Tilden Foundations, New York: Fig. I. Photography by The New York Public Library, Photographic Services.

Collection of The Heckscher Museum, Huntington, New York: Frontispiece. Photography by William Titus.

Courtesy of The Jorgensen Auditorium/Gallery, The University of Connecticut, Storrs, Connecticut; and Alpha Gallery, Boston, Massachusetts: Fig. XIX. Photography by Eric Pollitzer.

Courtesy of Mason Fine Prints, Glen Head, New York: L. 17; 20. Photography by Eric Pollitzer.

Courtesy of Mrs. Fairfield Porter, Southampton, New York: Fig. III; IV. Photography by Bolotsky; L. 1; 8, first and second states; 9; 10; 16; Fig. V; VI; VII; VIII; IX; X; XI; XVI; XVII (with the permission of Ted Berrigan). Photography by Eric Pollitzer.

Courtesy of Mrs. Fairfield Porter. Southampton, New York, from the Fairfield Porter Papers, Archives of American Art, Washington, D.C.: Fig. II; L. 4, 5, 6, 7. Photography by Smithsonian Institution, Office of Printing and Photographic Services.

Courtesy of Mrs. Fairfield Porter, Southampton, New York; from the John Wheelwright Papers, Brown University Library, Providence, Rhode Island: L. 2; 3. Photography by Brown University Photographic Laboratory.

Courtesy of Random House, Inc., New York: Fig. XIII; XIV; XV. Photography by Eric Pollitzer.

Courtesy of Special Projects Group, publisher of the Bicentennial Art Posters, Chicago, Illinois: Fig. XII. Photography by Eric Pollitzer.

Courtesy of Tatistcheff and Company, Inc., New York; David Hamilton Gallery, Charleston, South Carolina; and Mrs. Fairfield Porter: Fig. XX. Photography by Eric Pollitzer.

Courtesy of The Tibor de Nagy Gallery, New York, and David Workman: Fig. XVIII. Photography by Eric Pollitzer.

Courtesy of The William Benton Museum of Art, The University of Connecticut, Storrs, Connecticut: Fig. XXI. Photography by Eric Pollitzer.

SELECTED BIBLIOGRAPHY

The citations within this selective bibliography reflect a rapidly growing Porter literature. Included are books on his life, his work, and his writings; critical reviews and articles from art periodicals and newspapers; museum collection catalogues; gallery and dealer catalogues; exhibition catalogues; publications in which his illustrations appeared; and works in preparation. Though several works listed are solely concerned with the paintings, the major emphasis is placed on the graphic *oeuvre*.

The Archives of American Art, Smithsonian Institution, in Washington, D.C. is an unparalleled repository of Porter material consisting of published and unpublished documents, catalogues, letters, articles, sketchbooks, notebooks and ephemera. Microfilms of the collection are available at the Archive branch office in New York. Also in the Archives is the manuscript of the invaluable 1968 interview with Fairfield Porter conducted by Paul Cummings, which will forever serve as the basis for all research by Porter scholars.

The John Wheelwright Collection at the John Hay Library of Brown University, Providence, Rhode Island, is the primary source for the correspondence between Fairfield Porter and John Wheelwright, as well as for copies of the *Vanguard Verse* publications of the 1930s.

The Chicago Society of Artists *Artists' Calendars* can be found in the Print Room of the New York Public Library.

BOOKS

Arthur, John. *Realist Drawings and Watercolors: Contemporary American Works on Paper.* Boston: New York Graphic Society, 1980.

Cummings, Paul. *Artists in their own Words: Conversations with 12 American Artists.* New York: St. Martin's Press, 1979.

Downes, Rackstraw, ed. *Fairfield Porter: Art in its own terms—Selected Criticism 1935-1975.* New York: Taplinger Publishing Company, 1979.

Geske, Norman A. *Venice 34: The Figurative Tradition in Recent American Art.* Washington, D.C.: National Collection of Fine Arts/Smithsonian Institution Press, 1968.

Gussow, Alan. *A Sense of Place: The Artist and the American Land.* San Francisco; New York: Friends of the Earth: Seabury Press, 1971.

Knigin, Michael and Zimiles, Murray. *The Contemporary Lithographic Workshop Around the World.* New York: Van Nostrand Reinhold, 1974.

Porter, Eliot. *Summer Island, Penobscot Country.* Edited by David Brower. San Francisco: Sierra Club, 1966. New York: Ballantine Books/Random House, first revised printing, 1976.

Sandler, Irving. *The New York School: The Painters and Sculptors of the Fifties.* New York: Harper and Row, 1978.

Shapiro, David, ed. *Social Realism: Art as a Weapon.* New York: Frederick Ungar Publishing Company, 1973.

Tighe, Mary Ann and Elizabeth E. Lang. *Art America.* New York: McGraw-Hill Book Company, 1977.

Yochim, Louise Dunn. *Role and Impact: The Chicago Society of Artists.* Foreword by Harold Haydon. Chicago: The Chicago Society of Artists, 1979.

PERIODICALS

Andre, Michael. "Fairfield Porter: Isle au Haut," in "New Editions." *ARTnews* 74, no. 7 (September 1975): 56.

Ashbery, John. "Fairfield Porter, 1907-75." *Art in America* 64, no. 1 (January-February 1976): 20.

Berlind, Robert. "Fairfield Porter at Hirschl and Adler." *Art in America* 68, No. 2 (February 1980): 133.

Cummings, Paul. "Fairfield Porter." *Archives of American Art Journal* 12, no. 2 (1972). 10-21.

Cummings, Paul. "An Interview with Fairfield Porter." *American Artist* 39, no. 393 (April 1975): 34-39.

Downes, Rackstraw. "Fairfield Porter: The Painter as Critic." *Art Journal* 37, no. 4 (Summer 1978): 306-312.

Finkelstein, Louis. "The Naturalness of Fairfield Porter." *Arts Magazine* 50, no. 9 (May 1976): 102-105.

Goldman, Judith. "Exploring the possibilities of the Print Medium." *ARTnews* 72, no. 7 (September 1973): 35.

Henning, Edward B. "South of His House, North of His House: Nyack; A Painting by Fairfield Porter." *The Bulletin of The Cleveland Museum of Art* (March 1971): 85-90.

Hess, Thomas. "Fairfield Porter." *New York Magazine* (December 22, 1975).

Mainardi, Patricia. "Fairfield Porter's Contribution to Modernism." *ARTnews* 75, no. 2 (February 1976): 109.

Myers, John Bernard. "Fairfield Porter (1907-1975) *Parenthese* 3 (1975): 187-189.

O'Hara, Frank. "Porter paints a picture." *ARTnews* 53, No. 9 (January 1955): 38-41, 66-67.

Perl, Jed. "Fairfield Porter." *Arts Magazine* 54, no. 6 (February 1980): 4.

Perlmutter, Elizabeth Frank. "New Editions." *ARTnews* 73, no. 7 (September 1974): 53.

"Prints and Portfolios Published," *Print Collector's Newsletter* 2, no. 2 (May-June 1971): 35.

"Prints and Portfolios Published," *Print Collector's Newsletter* 2, no. 3 (July-August 1971): 57.

"Prints and Portfolios Published," *Print Collector's Newsletter* 2, no. 4 (September-October 1971): 86-87.

"Prints and Portfolios Published," *Print Collector's Newsletter* 4, no. 4 (September-October 1973): 86.

"Prints and Portfolios Published," *Print Collector's Newsletter* 6, no. 1 (March-April 1975): 16

"Prints and Portfolios Published." *Print Collector's Newsletter* 6, no. 4 (September-October 1975): 108.

Schuyler, James. "Immediacy is the Message." *ARTnews* 66, no. 1 (March 1967).

Shapiro, David. "Paying Attention: Fairfield Porter's Watercolors." *57th Street Review*, supplement (December 1975): 8b-8f.

Wahl, Kenneth. "Fairfield Porter Dec. 2-Jan. 6." *57th Street Review* (December 1975): 12-13.

NEWSPAPER ARTICLES

Beem, E.A. "People and Things Connected—Fairfield Porter: Creator And Critic." *Portland Independent* (Portland, Maine): July 27, 1979. Pages 17-19.

Glueck, Grace. "Nature—with Manners." *The New York Times*, January 19, 1969.

Kramer, Hilton. "Fairfield Porter: Against the Historical Grain." *The New York Times*, February 20, 1966.

Kramer, Hilton. "An Art of Conservation." *The New York Times*, February 9, 1969.

Kramer, Hilton. "Chase, Porter and History." *The New York Times*, May 14, 1976.

Kramer, Hilton. "Why Figurative Art Confounds Our Museums." *The New York Times*, January 2, 1977, page 19 D.

Kramer, Hilton. "Porter—A Virtuoso Colorist." *The New York Times*, November 25, 1979, page 23, 32.

O'Doherty, Brian. "By Fairfield Porter: His School of Paris Works, Which Bring the Outdoors In, Shown at de Nagy's." *The New York Times*, March 24, 1964.

Oxorn, Pearl. "Fairfield Porter." *The Washington Star*, December 16, 1979, page C 2.

Paris, Jeanne. "Different views—LI painters Show their Prints." *Long Island Press*, September 1, 1974, page 18.

Preston, Malcolm. "Porter without flair." *Newsday* (Garden City, N.Y.): September 11, 1973.

Preston, Malcolm, "Painters' Prints." *Newsday* (Garden City, N.Y.): September 6, 1974.

Preston, Malcolm, "Porter in Maine." *Newsday* (Garden City, N.Y.): August 22, 1977, page 30 A.

Preston, Malcolm. "Down to the sea in paintings." *Newsday* (Garden City, N.Y.): August 20, 1980, page II 60.

Richard, Paul. "Strokes of City Light: Fairfield Porter's Window on New York." *The Washington Post*, December 15, 1979, page C 1, C 7.

Russell, John. "Trapping the Look of New York." *The New York Times* April 24, 1977, page 25.

Schneider, Howard. "Me, by Fairfield Porter—and Vice Versa." *Newsday, L.I. Magazine* (Garden City, N.Y.); February 17, 1974, pages 8-10, 20, 28-29.

Shirey, David. "Porter's Works on Display." *The New York Times,* December 22, 1974, page 4BQLI.

MUSEUM COLLECTION CATALOGUES

Amherst College, Mead Art Gallery. *American Art at Amherst: A Summary Catalogue of the Collection.* Catalogue by Lewis A. Shepard with David Paley. Distributed by Wesleyan University Press, Middletown, Conn., 1978.

Brooklyn Museum, The. *The Brooklyn Museum American Paintings.* Foreword by Michael Botwinick; Preface by Sarah Faunce; Introduction by Linda S. Ferber. Brooklyn, N.Y., 1979.

Heckscher Museum, The. *Catalogue of the Collection.* American Collection catalogue by Ronald G. Pisano, European Collection catalogue by Carol Forman Tabler. Introduction by S. Katherine Lochridge. Huntington, N.Y., 1979.

Museum of Modern Art, The. *Painting and Sculpture in the Museum of Modern Art 1929-1967.* Catalogue by Alfred H. Barr, Jr. New York, 1977.

Museum of Modern Art, The. *Painting and Sculpture in the Museum of Modern Art, with selected works on paper; Catalog of the Collection January 1, 1977.* Edited by Alicia Legg. New York, 1977.

New Britain Museum of American Art, The. *Catalogue of the Collection.* New Britain, Conn., 1975.

Whitney Museum of American Art, The. *Catalogue of the Collection.* Catalogue by Margaret McKellar, Elke Solomon and Mariann Nowack. Introduction by John I.H. Baur. New York, 1974.

MUSEUM AND GALLERY EXHIBITION CATALOGUES

Associated American Artists. *New York, New York.* New York, August 5-September 30, 1974.

Barridoff Galleries. *Fairfield Porter.* Essay by Rackstraw Downes. Portland, Maine, July 23-September 3, 1979.

Boston University Art Gallery. *Brooke Alexander—A Decade of Print Publishing.* Essay by Judith Goldman. Exhibition organized by John Arthur. Boston, Mass., November 27-December 22, 1978.

Colby College Art Museum. *Fairfield Porter Paintings—Eliot Porter Photographs.* Essay by James M. Carpenter. Waterville, Maine, May 6-June 2, 1969.

Harbor Gallery. *Fairfield Porter.* Cold Spring Harbor, N.Y., August 19-September 15, 1973.

Harbor Gallery. *Fairfield Porter.* Introduction by Claire Nicolas White. Cold Spring Harbor, N.Y., March 13-April 16, 1977.

Harbor Gallery. *A Selection of Great Prints.* Vol. 4. Cold Spring Harbor, New York, December 9, 1979-February 28, 1980.

Heckscher Museum, The. *Artists of Suffolk County, Part VI: Contemporary Prints.* Introduction by Ruth Solomon. Huntington, N.Y. July 16-September 3, 1972.

Heckscher Museum, The. *Fairfield Porter Retrospective Exhibition.* Essay by Eva Ingersoll Gatling. Huntington, N.Y. December 15, 1974-January 26, 1975; Queens Museum, N.Y., February 7-March 9, 1975; Montclair Art Museum, N.J., March 23-April 27, 1975.

Hirschl and Adler Gallery, Inc. *Recent Work by Fairfield Porter.* Introduction by Peter Schjeldahl. New York, April 11-April 29, 1972.

Hirschl and Adler Gallery, Inc. *Recent Work by Fairfield Porter.* New York, March 2-March 23, 1974.

Hirschl and Adler Gallery, Inc. *Fairfield Porter—His Last Works 1974-1975.* Introduction by Prescott Schutz. May 4-May 28, 1976.

Library of Congress and the National Collection of Fine Arts. *Catalog—25th National Exhibition of Prints.* Washington, D.C., May 27-September 18, 1977.

Mickelson Gallery. *Fairfield Porter 1907-1975: Prints and Paintings.* Washington, D.C., December 3, 1979-January 28, 1980.

Neuberger Museum, State University of New York. *In Celebration: Selections from the Private Collection of Roy R. and Marie S. Neuberger.* Purchase, N.Y., September 24-November 26, 1978.

Parrish Art Museum, The. *Fairfield Porter's Maine.* Introduction by Helen A. Harrison. Southampton, N.Y., July-September 1977.

Parrish Art Museum, The. *The Porter Family.* Essay by Philip Ferrato. Southampton, N.Y., May-June 1980.

United States Department of the Interior. *America 1976: A Bicentennial Exhibition sponsored by the U.S. Department of the Interior.* Washington, D.C., April 27, 1976-May 21, 1978.

Whitney Museum of American Art, The. *Selections from the Lawrence Bloedel Bequest and Related Works from the Permanent Collection of the Whitney Museum of American Art.* New York, April 5-June 19, 1977.

Whitney Museum of American Art, The. *New York on Paper.* Introduction by Judith Goldman. New York, April 7-May 22, 1977.

Worcester Art Museum. Worcester Art Museum Bulletin, *Two Decades of American Printmaking: 1957-1977.* Worcester, Mass., March 15-May 14, 1978.

GALLERY, DEALER AND AUCTION CATALOGUES

Brooke Alexander, Inc. Illustrated Print List. New York, December 1971.

Brooke Alexander, Inc. Illustrated Print List. New York, October 1972.

Brooke Alexander, Inc. and The Skowhegan School of Painting and Sculpture. Brochure. New York, 1973.

Brooke Alexander, Inc. Illustrated Print List. New York, 1974.

Brooke Alexander, Inc. *Selected Prints 1960-1977.* New York, 1977.

Aldis Brown Fine Arts, Ltd. Catalogue. New York, 1974.

Christie's. *19th and 20th Century Prints.* New York, November 16, 1978.

Christie's. *19th and 20th Century Prints.* New York, September 29, 1979.

Collectors Graphics. Catalogue and List. New York: Peridot Gallery (c. 1962).

Knoedler and Company, Inc. *Lithographs by de Kooning, Fairfield Porter, Paul Waldman.* New York, 1971.

Mason Fine Prints. *Catalogue no. 21: Blue Chip Prints.* Glen Head, N.Y. 1979.

Shorewood-Bank Street Atelier. *Ten Lithographs by Ten Artists Published for the Skowhegan School.* Brochure. New York, 1971.

Sotheby Parke Bernet Inc. *Nineteenth and Twentieth Century Prints–Old Master Prints.* New York, February 15-16, 1979.

Sotheby Parke Bernet Inc. *Contemporary Art.* New York, October 19, 1979.

Sotheby Parke Bernet, Inc. *Nineteenth and Twentieth Century Prints–Contemporary Prints.* New York, December 18-19, 1979.

Special Projects Group. *1776 U.S.A. 1976.* Chicago, Ill., 1975.

ENCYCLOPEDIAS AND BIOGRAPHICAL DICTIONARIES

Baigell, Matthew. *Dictionary of American Art.* New York: Harper and Row, 1979.

Britannica Encyclopedia of American Art, The. Chicago: Encyclopedia Britannica Educational Corporation, 1974.

Cummings, Paul. *Dictionary of Contemporary American Artists.* New York: St. Martin's Press, 1966.

Cummings, Paul. *Dictionary of Contemporary American Artists.* Second edition. New York: St. Martin's Press, 1971.

Phaidon Dictionary of 20th Century Art. Second edition. Oxford, England: Phaidon Press Limited; New York: E.P. Dutton, 1977.

Phaidon Encyclopedia of Art and Artists. Oxford, England: Phaidon Press Limited; New York: E.P. Dutton, 1978.

Who's Who in American Art 1970. Edited by Dorothy B. Gilbert. New York: R.R. Bowker Company, 1970.

Who's Who in American Art 1973. Edited by The Jaques Cattell Press. Foreword by Wilder Green. New York and London: Jaques Cattell Press/R.R. Bowker Company, 1973.

POETRY PAMPHLETS

Poems for a Dime 4 (January 8, 1936).

Poems for a Dime 5 (November 25, 1936).

Poems for a Dime 6 (November 7, 1937).

Poems for 2 Bits 3 (June 16, 1936).

OTHER SOURCES

Artists' Calendar 1939. Chicago, Ill.: Chicago Society of Artists/Boss-Stolberg, 1938.

Artists' Calendar 1940. Introduction by Helen Forman, Art Department, Chicago Public Library. Chicago, Ill.; Chicago Society of Artists, 1939.

Castleman, Riva. *Introduction* to the Portfolio "Ten Lithographs by Ten Artists." New York: Bank Street Atelier, Ltd., 1971.

WORKS IN PREPARATION

Ferrato, Philip. *Catalogue Raisonne of the Paintings of Fairfield Porter.* New York, *forthcoming.*

Wald, Alan. *John Wheelwright and Sherry Mangan: The Marxist Experience of Two Harvard Poets.* Ann Arbor, Mich., *forthcoming.*

TITLE INDEX

(Listings are by catalogue number. Alternate titles appear in parentheses.)

continued on page 156

INDEX

Bold face number indicates page on which illustration appears.

158

Fairfield Porter: A Catalogue Raisonné of His Prints
was designed by Kristine Knapp Czarnecki.
The book was printed on seventy pound Hammermill White Lustre paper
by The Book Press, Inc. Brattleboro, Vermont,
and bound in one piece Devon by The Book Press, Inc.
Color separations and four color printing on one hundred pound Longacre Gloss
was by The Longacre Press, Inc. New Rochelle, New York.
The type was set by DH Graphics, Valhalla, N.Y.

The book was produced under the editorial direction
of Benedict A. Leerburger.

The type face is Garth Graphic,
a 20th century face selected to reflect
the contemporary nature of Porter's works.
The type, designed by Renée LeWinter and
Constance Blanchard in 1977, was named for William W. Garth, Jr.
co-founder of Compugraphics, Inc.
a manufacturer of phototypesetting equipment.

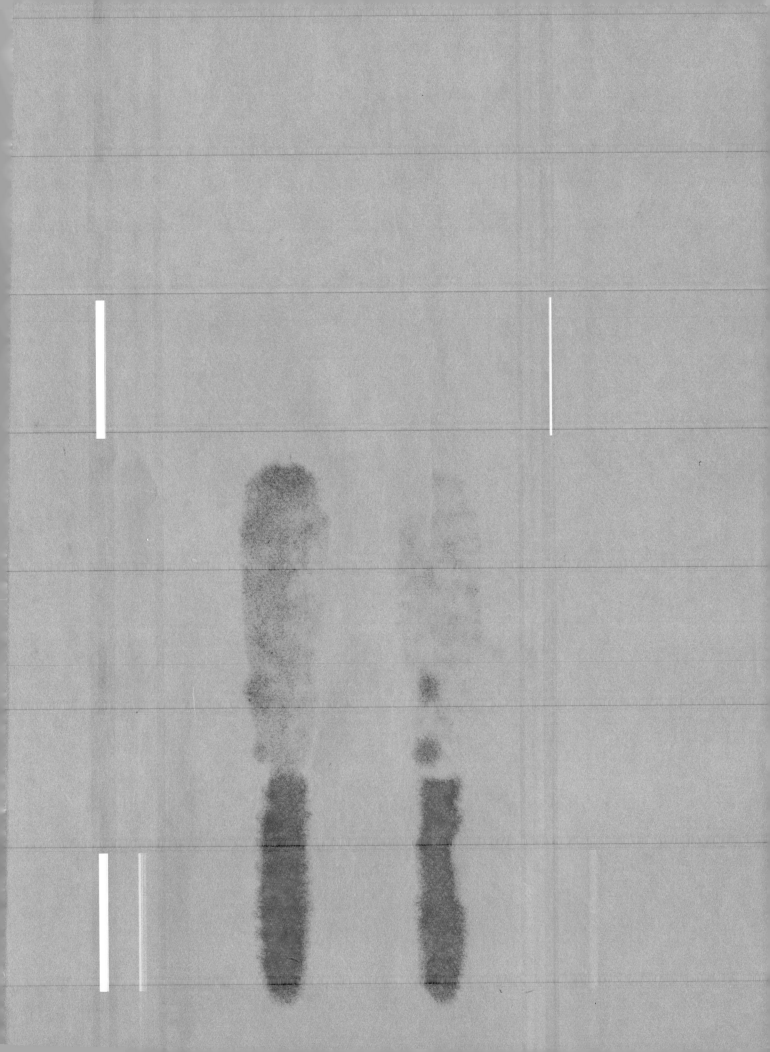

DATE DUE

SEP 29 2003	
GAYLORD	PRINTED IN U.S.A.